D1329750

INTERNATIONAL SERIES OF MONOGRAPHS ON
PURE AND APPLIED BIOLOGY

Division: **BOTANY**

GENERAL EDITORS: R. C. ROLLINS AND G. TAYLOR

VOLUME 4

CORK

AND THE CORK TREE

WITHDRAWN
FROM THE
CARL B. YLVISAKER LIBRARY
Concordia College, Moorhead, MN

(*Courtesy, Crown Cork & Seal Co.*)

A cork forest in Portugal. Recently stripped cork has been placed in stacks.

CORK

AND THE CORK TREE

BY

GILES B. COOKE, Ph.D.

CONSULTING CHEMIST

Formerly Research Chemist
for Armstrong Cork Company
and Director of Research
for Crown Cork & Seal Company

WITHDRAWN
FROM THE
CARL B. YLVISAKER LIBRARY
Concordia College, Moorhead, MN

PERGAMON PRESS

NEW YORK . OXFORD . LONDON . PARIS

1961

SD
397
.C79C59

PERGAMON PRESS INC.
122 East 55th Street, New York 22, N.Y.
Statler Center 640, 900 Wilshire Boulevard
Los Angeles 17, California

PERGAMON PRESS LTD.
Headington Hill Hall, Oxford
4 & 5 Fitzroy Square, London W.1

PERGAMON PRESS S.A.R.L.
24 Rue des Écoles, Paris V[e]

PERGAMON PRESS G.m.b.H.
Kaiserstrasse 75, Frankfurt am Main

Copyright
©
1961
PERGAMON PRESS INC.

Library of Congress Card Number 61-9780

Set in Bembo 12 on 13 pt. and printed in Great Britain at
THE CAMPFIELD PRESS, ST. ALBANS, ENGLAND

TO MY WIFE, ANNA, AND
DAUGHTER, ANN DORSEY

this book is

affectionately dedicated

ACKNOWLEDGMENT

The author wishes to express his thanks and gratitude to the many persons and various organizations whose cooperation have made this book possible. While space does not permit reference to all who have been helpful, mention should be made of Mr. Joseph J. Waters, Director of Research, and Mr. Frank J. Feild, Research Department, Crown Cork & Seal Company, who read the manuscript and offered valuable suggestions. For assisting with the botanical characteristics of cork, special thanks are due to Dr. John T. Baldwin, Jr., Professor of Biology, College of William and Mary. To my secretary, Miss Gloria Dickens, for her faithful and patient assistance in typing the manuscript, I am most grateful. Credit has been acknowledged with the illustrations and tables of statistics.

CONTENTS

PART II. CORK CULTURE IN THE UNITED STATES

PREFACE

THE author's purpose in writing this book is to provide a single source for the important general information about cork. While the literature on cork and the tree from which it is obtained is somewhat limited, numerous items on the botany, chemistry, physical properties and applications of cork have appeared from time to time. In this book the facts previously recorded are incorporated with the author's firsthand knowledge gained in over 30 years of experience with cork, cork trees and the cork industry.

In order to give the reader a complete story an historical review is presented first. Then follows in order the geographical distribution, a description of the tree, its cultivation and the harvesting of the cork bark. A discussion on the botanical aspects of the cork tree is given, and the characteristics of the tree and methods of its culture are presented. Before taking the reader into the manufacture of cork products and the applications of cork, the very important physical and chemical properties are discussed.

Some figures on world trade and production of cork are presented. These are of particular interest for they show the rise in cork production during the past 60 years as well as the increase in the manufacture of cork products during the same period.

Efforts to grow the cork tree outside of its natural habitat are presented. Special emphasis is given to the planting and growing of cork trees in the United States through the McManus Cork Project.

The author hopes this book will be of value to the many users of cork products in telling them about the source and properties of this essential commodity. He hopes other readers will become more conscious of the importance of cork and develop a greater appreciation of this unusual natural product and the tree from which it comes.

Since the cork oak is an evergreen and makes an attractive ornamental shade tree many of those who are being introduced to it for the first time may wish to grow several cork trees. For this reason directions for planting and suggestions for the care of young cork oaks are given.

Certainly a material with such an impressive record over so many years deserves more than casual attention. Better acquaintance with cork and more knowledge of it by more people will result in further technical developments and consequently further industrial applications. The more we know about cork the greater will be the benefits derived from it by mankind.

GILES B. COOKE

Towson, Maryland

CHAPTER I

INTRODUCTION AND HISTORY

A brotherhood of venerable trees.
WILLIAM WORDSWORTH

INTRODUCTION

Cork is the bark of the cork oak tree, *Quercus suber*, which is indigenous to those countries that form the shores of the western Mediterranean. Portugal, Spain, France and Italy in Europe and Algeria, Morocco and Tunisia in Africa are the cork-producing countries of the world. When the cork oak attains proper size the cork bark is removed, "stripped", without injuring the tree and new cork grows to replace it. This process is repeated every 8 to 10 years. For more than 2000 years practically all the cork for the world's commerce has come from sections of these countries. The cork forests total about 5,000,000 acres, an area approximately the size of the state of Connecticut. The greater portion of these forests is of natural origin. Here for centuries cork forests have withstood the ravages of wind, fire, war and other destructive forces without any substantial assistance from man. Only in comparatively recent years has particular attention been given to the care of these very important cork forests. Removal of fire-promoting undergrowth and reforestation in desirable areas have become the standard practice. Also, regulations governing the conditions for stripping and the exercise of special care in removing the cork have preserved the vitality of the trees, extending their productive life and increasing the quality and quantity of cork.

For centuries cork has been employed by man to serve special needs. During ancient times these uses were few and simple but as civilization advanced the applications of cork expanded and kept pace with man's progress. In our modern, complex life of today cork performs numerous essential services although it is often both unseen and unknown by those it serves. The natural material in the form of slabs which have been carefully graded are cut and shaped into many important articles.

Hundreds of applications utilize products of composition cork which is manufactured from small particles of cork, produced and known in the trade as granulated cork.

In a highly technological age, with scientific developments crowding one after the other in a continuous stream of achievements, it is interesting to review a product of nature that holds so long a record of uninterrupted service to mankind. From 400 B.C., and perhaps earlier, to the present time, a period of over 2350 years, cork has been a useful, needed plant product. Today, cork is still employed for many of the uses for which it served mankind centuries ago and, in addition, is specified as an essential material in some of our very recent developments.

This product of nature, therefore, justly deserves attention. Through century after century a piece of cork has been the preferred material for

(*Courtesy, Crown Cork & Seal Co.*)

Cork readily separates from the inner bark. Note the type of stripping hatchet employed.

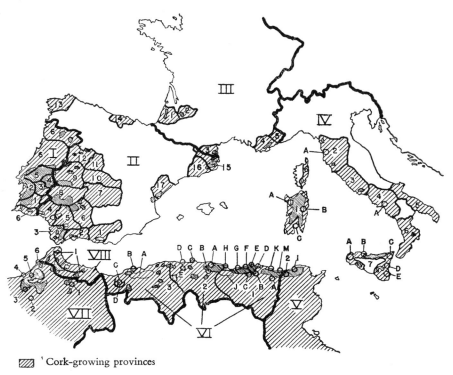

☑ ' Cork-growing provinces

▨ Location of cork forests

(Courtesy, Smithsonian Institution)

The cork forest area of the western Mediterranean, where the world's supply of cork is produced.

KEY

I. PORTUGAL

Number				Province
1	.	.	.	Beja
2	.	.	.	Setubal
3	.	.	.	Evora
4	.	.	.	Portalegre
5	.	.	.	Santarem
6	.	.	.	All others

II. SPAIN

1	.	.	.	Granada
2	.	.	.	Malaga
3	.	.	.	Cadiz
4	.	.	.	Huelva
5	.	.	.	Sevilla
6	.	.	.	Cordoba
7	.	.	.	Ciudad Real
8	.	.	.	Badajoz
9	.	.	.	Cáceres
10	.	.	.	Toledo
11	.	.	.	Avila
12	.	.	.	Salamanca
13	.	.	.	Coruna
14	.	.	.	Santander
15	.	.	.	Gerona
16	.	.	.	Barcelona
17	.	.	.	Castellon

III. FRANCE

				Department
1	.	.	.	Landes
2	.	.	.	Lot-et-Garonne
3	.	.	.	Pyrenées-Orientales
4	.	.	.	Var
5	.	.	.	Alpes-Maritimes
6	.	.	.	Corsica

IV. ITALY

				District or Province
1	.	.	.	Sardinia
1-A	.	.	.	Sassari
1-B	.	.	.	Nuoro
1-C	.	.	.	Cagliari
2	.	.	.	Tuscany
2-A	.	.	.	Pisa
3	.	.	.	Latium
4	.	.	.	Compania
4-A	.	.	.	Salerno
5	.	.	.	Apulia
6	.	.	.	Calabria
7	.	.	.	Sicily
7-A	.	.	.	Trapani

Number				District or Province
7-B	.	.	.	Palermo
7-C	.	.	.	Messina
7-D	.	.	.	Catania
7-E	.	.	.	Syracuse

V. TUNISIA

				Region
1	.	.	.	Mogods
2	.	.	.	Khroumiria

VI. ALGERIA

1	.	.	.	Dep. of Constantine
1-A	.	.	.	Souk-Ahras
1-B	.	.	.	Jemmapes
1-C	.	.	.	Sidi-Meroun
1-D	.	.	.	Philippeville
1-E	.	.	.	Collo
1-F	.	.	.	El Melia
1-G	.	.	.	Djidjelli
1-H	.	.	.	Bougie
1-J	.	.	.	Jebel (Mts.) of Babors
1-K	.	.	.	Bona
1-M	.	.	.	La Calle
2	.	.	.	Dep. of Algiers
2-A	.	.	.	Drael-Mizan
2-B	.	.	.	Bouira
2-C	.	.	.	Algiers
2-D	.	.	.	Cherchel
2-E	.	.	.	Militana
3	.	.	.	Dep. of Oran
3-A	.	.	.	Sahel of Oran
3-B	.	.	.	Oran
3-C	.	.	.	Tlemcen
3-D	.	.	.	Jebel Tlemcen

VII. FRENCH MOROCCO

1	.	.	.	Taza, near forest of Bab Azhar
2	.	.	.	Tedders, near groves of The Zemmour
3	.	.	.	Marchand, near groves of The Zaer
4	.	.	.	Sale, near forest of The Sehouls
5	.	.	.	Mamora
6	.	.	.	Moulay Bou-Selham, near Forest of Gharb

VIII. SPANISH MOROCCO

1	.	.	.	Line of the Riff Mountains

sealing jars, jugs and bottles. So long and so well has cork performed this service that the words "to stopper" and "to cork" have acquired the same meaning. So excellently has cork performed its various services, the word cork itself is sometimes used to express superior characteristics. The phrase "corking good" is a term applied generally to express very high quality. A large meat packing company in the eastern part of the United States has often advertised its famous sugar-cured hams as "corking good".

What characteristics does cork possess that enable it not only to hold but also to enlarge its field of applications through so long a period of time? The answer to this question is given in the discussion of the characteristics of cork and its applications that are presented in the pages which follow. It is interesting to note that substitutes for cork for certain particular applications have been developed, but these are limited to the special use for which they were designed. Up to the present time no general substitute for cork has been brought forward and cork still stands as a challenge to our progressive and highly inventive age.

HISTORY

Cork is a very old plant product measured in years of service to mankind. One of the oldest written records of its use dates back to about 400 B.C., but without doubt this light, thick bark was used many centuries earlier. Natives in the cork-producing countries have from the earliest times used cork bark to serve their various needs. Just what the early people of the Iberian Peninsula thought of cork 4000 or 5000 years ago and how they used it would make interesting reading. It is fascinating to speculate and safe to guess that cork was employed then for some of its present-day applications.

The early Greeks and Romans were familiar with cork, and in the classic works of ancient and medieval writers numerous references to it can be found. Plutarch (A.D. 46–120), in his famous *Parallel Lives*, II, XXV, 154, Life of Camillus (Marcus Furius Camillus, 446–365 B.C.), tells of the use of cork as an aid in swimming. When Rome was besieged by the Gauls about 400 B.C., Camillus was named dictator, and it was necessary to obtain the approval of his selection by the Senate, the members of which were imprisoned in the Capitol. A youth, Pontius Cominius,

B

volunteered to carry the message, and as the bridge across the Tiber was guarded by the enemy he swam the river at night. We read:

> But there was a certain young man, Pontius Cominius by name, who was, in spite of his ordinary birth, a lover of glory and honor. He volunteered to attempt the task. He took no letter with him to the defenders of the Capitol, lest this, in the event of his capture, should help the enemy to discover the purpose of Camillus; but under the coarse garments which he wore, he carried some pieces of cork. The greater part of his journey was made by daylight and without fear; but as night came on he found himself near the city. He could not cross the river by the bridge, since the Barbarians were guarding it, so he wrapped his light and scanty garments about his head, fastened the corks to his body, and thus supported, swam across, came out on the other side, and went on towards the city. [1]

Pliny the Elder (*ca.* A.D. 23–79), gives a detailed description of the cork tree and its utilization in his famous *Naturalis Historia*, XVI. In Section 13 he writes that it is a small tree with evergreen leaves, bearing small acorns, and he further states:

> Its only useful product is its bark, which is extremely thick and which when cut grows again; when flattened out it has been known to form a sheet as big as 10 square feet. This bark is used chiefly for ships' anchor drag ropes and fishermen's drag nets and for the bungs of casks, and also to make soles for women's winter shoes. Consequently the Greek name for the tree is "bark-tree", which is not inappropriate. [2]

Other famous Romans also wrote about cork, telling of varied uses for the material. Horace (65–8 B.C.), in his classic works, refers to wine casks being sealed with cork. The Romans in the process of aging wine subjected casks to smoke and, according to custom, dated the wine and recorded the name of the Consul on the cask. In Horace's *Odes*, Book III, Ode 8, we read:

> *Hic dies anno redunte festus*
> *Corticem adstrictum pice dimovebit*
> *Amphorar fumum bibere institutae Concule Tullo.*
>
> ("This day, sacred in the revolving year,
> shall remove the cork fastened with pitch
> from that jar, which was set to inhale
> the smoke in the Consulship of Tullus.") [3]

Columella (about A.D. 20–75) referred to cork in the making of bee-hives. In an English translation we read:

. . . Bee-hives must be fabricated according to the condition and circumstances of the country. For if it is fertile of the cork tree, without any doubt we may make very useful hives of its bark, because they are neither extremely cold in winter, nor exceedingly hot in summer.[4]

In the classic writings of Virgil reference is made to cork. We find in *The Aeneid*, Book VII, a section in which Aeneas describes the soldiers of one of the armies of ancient Latium. In this account Aeneas states:

Their head covering was stripped bark of the cork tree.[5]

Theophrastus (372–287 B.C.) was the first Greek author to describe the cork oak. In his famous work on botany, he wrote:

Some, however, are more local, such as the cork oak; this occurs in Tyrrhenia; it is a tree with a distinct trunk and few branches, and is fairly tall and of vigorous growth. The wood is strong; the bark very thick and cracked, like that of the Aleppo pine, save that the cracks are larger. The leaf is like that of the manna-ash, thick and somewhat oblong. The tree is not evergreen but deciduous. It has always an acorn-like fruit like that of the aria (holm-oak). They strip off the bark, and they say that it should all be removed, otherwise the tree deteriorates. It is renewed again in about three years.[6]

This description of the cork oak by Theophrastus is in general correct. In areas where winter weather is mild the leaves of the tree are green during the winter and new ones appear with the return of warmer weather in the spring. Some cork oak acorns are small, but from the large scattered old trees they are of good size and resemble acorns of the white oak, *Quercus alba*. While the bark begins new growth shortly after the stripping, 8 to 10 years instead of 3 years are needed to make the growth of 1 in. to 2 in. required for commercial cork.

Theophrastus describes the cork tree and refers to the hard outside portion of the bark. He does not discuss cork and its applications, but the Greeks were familiar with its characteristics and made practical use of this unique bark. Pausanias, traveller and geographer of the second century A.D., in his Report VIII, referring to the oak trees of Arcadia, wrote:

The oaks in the groves of the Arcadians are of different sorts; some of them are called "broad-leaved", others "edible oaks". A third kind have a porous bark, which is so light that they actually make from it floats for anchors and nets. The bark of this oak is called "cork" by the Ionians.[7]

Spanish writers make frequent references to their native and valuable cork oak. Cervantes, 1547–1616, in *Don Quixote* refers to the cork tree on several occasions. We read in Chapter XI, as Don Quixote soliloquizes about the golden age of the ancients:

> The vigorous cork trees of their own free will and grace, without the asking, shed their broad light bark with which men began to cover their dwellings erected upon rude stakes merely as a protection against the inclemency of the heavens.[8]

Also, reference to the cork oak is found in Chapter XXIII as Don Quixote and his companions spend a night in a dense cork tree grove in the Sierra Morena mountains. In Part II, Chapter XIV, Sancha Panza climbs into a cork tree while Don Quixote duels with an opponent knight.

As time passed on cork continued to be used for sealing jars and casks. Shakespeare in one of his later plays refers to cork as a bung for hogsheads. In *The Winter's Tale*, Act III, the Clown compares a ship in a heavy sea, covered with froth and hidden from sight, to a cork forced into a foaming keg. We read:

> Now the ship boring the moon with mainmast, and anon swallowed with yest and froth, as you'ld thrust a cork into a hogshead.[9]

Another English reference tells of cork being tested for a possible new application. In Samuel Pepys's *Diary*, we read:

> That being done, I went down to Thames-streete and there agreed for four or five tons of corke, to send this day to the fleete, being a new device to make barricados with, instead of junke.[10]

For many centuries cork has been employed to keep heat in buildings during the winter season and keep it out in the hot summer months. The natural cork bark served this purpose in medieval times. Early monasteries were provided with cork-lined walls and ceilings to afford protection from the intense heat of the summer sun. Peasant natives in the cork-producing countries for centuries used cork slabs to roof their houses and to provide soft floors that were always warm and soft to the touch. In later times cork was mixed with earth and used to form the walls of buildings.

Through the years cork continued to be employed for such purposes and as its unique characteristics became better known and better understood its use expanded. New applications for cork were found and old ones became more widespread.

With the invention of the glass bottle in the fifteenth century and its more general introduction in the seventeenth century, the use of cork began to increase and the cork industry may be said to have started then. Cork forests that had been growing wild for centuries were recognized to have a definite commercial value. The first steps toward the cultivation of the cork oak tree were taken in Spain about 1760.[11] A German who had taken up his residence on the Spanish peninsula rented several cork forests, cleared away the undergrowth and supervised the harvesting of the bark. The cork was exported to Germany and sold there. Others, recognizing the profit to be had in such an enterprise, followed his example and by 1830 the cultivation of the cork oak had extended into France, Portugal, Italy and northern Africa.

CHAPTER II

THE CORK TREE

I like trees because they seem more resigned to
the way they have to live than other things do.

WILLA SIBERT CATHER

BOTANICAL CHARACTERISTICS

The cork tree is an oak known botanically as *Quercus suber*. Another
species of cork-producing oak, *Quercus occidentalis*, was described by
J. Gay, the Swiss botanist, in 1856. However, the two species are very
much alike and differ chiefly in the duration of their foliage and the ripening season of their fruits. *Quercus suber* is evergreen and produces annual
fruits; *Quercus occidentalis* usually drops its leaves in the spring and produces biennial fruits. Most of the cork of commerce comes from *Quercus
suber*, this species being the dominant tree of the large cork forests.
Quercus occidentalis is more cold-resistant and is found in northern sections
of Spain and Portugal where it withstands the cold winds of the Atlantic
and the lower winter temperatures prevalent in those areas.

The cork tree is a temperate zone plant and does not thrive in regions
having a tropical climate.[12] The cork-producing areas lie between the
mean annual temperatures of 50° and 70°F. However, cork trees are
occasionally found beyond these temperature limits.

The cork oak is very hardy and in forests grows to medium size. The
tree attains a height of from 40 ft to 60 ft and a bole circumference
ranging from 6 ft to 10 ft. Larger specimens are found, and when
grown in open fields the cork oak may reach a very substantial size.
Mammoth trees measuring 8 ft to 10 ft in diamater and over 50 ft in
height have been reported. Such manificent specimens are rare and
require many years, in fact several centuries, to reach such dimensions. A
beautiful cork tree at Napa, California, measures 58 inches in diameter, is
over 60 ft in height and has a limb spread of about 100 ft. This tree is
estimated to be about 100 years old.

In general the cork oak has a relatively short trunk and low, spreading branches. By careful pruning of a young tree a high, straight bole can be obtained. A few trees, because of light or other factors, develop a tall trunk with the lowest branches 15 ft or 20 ft from the ground. Throughout the cork forests a wide range of growth habits occur. In the United States, also, extreme differences in growth patterns have been found. At Fresno, California, a stout cork oak with a 44-in. diameter trunk has a 24-in. branch extending from the trunk just 2 ft above the ground. A few yards away stands another cork oak that has a tall, straight bole with the first branch about 20 ft from the ground. Such variations are not common and in the cork forests the trees—doubtless because of self-pruning—generally grow in a more uniform pattern.

The trunk of the cork oak is subject to internal decay, but old trees with large trunk cavities continue productive growth for many years. The mature tree has a long tap root with vigorous laterals. The spreading roots of old cork oaks often may be seen above the ground. This extensive and deep root system provides water and minerals during the long dry periods prevalent in the cork forest regions. Also, this strong root development is responsible, in part, for the "will to live" which is evidenced so definitely by the cork oak. When a tree is severely damaged above the ground, or even if the trunk is completely severed, new shoots will appear. Because of the well established root system, growth of the new shoot is vigorous and rapid.

The productive age of cork trees ranges from 100 to 200 years with an average of 150 years. When a tree ceases to yield profitably, it is removed. The heart wood is dark, while the sapwood is lighter. The cork oak has usually been considered to be in the subgenus with the white oaks. Recently, Williams has shown the wood of the cork tree to have anatomical features similar to those of the red oak.[13] The wood is compact, heavy and difficult to work. The density varies from 0.803 to 1.029.[14]

While drying, the wood is subject to much warping and deep splitting. It is not suitable for construction purposes because of its generally short length. The seasoned wood is employed for manufacturing tool handles and other small wooden objects. A large percentage of the wood is converted to charcoal, much of which is used for heating homes in the cork-producing countries.

The cork oak is monoecious. In the spring, usually April or May—the exact time depending on the climate of the location in which the trees are growing and the weather during the season—the yellow flowers appear. Against the dark foliage they give the cork tree a delightful appearance. The male flowers develop at the end of the previous year's growth. They are in thread-like catkins which occur in groups. The female flowers are in the axils of the leaves, on the new growth, and are small, scaly and cup-shaped. A small red tuft, the stigma, terminates the flower.

The leaves resemble those of the English holly but are soft to the touch. They are ovate to ovate-oblong and rounded or tublordate at the base. They measure from $1\frac{1}{4}$ in. to 2 in., with the width varying from $1\frac{1}{2}$ in. to $1\frac{1}{4}$ in. During the fruiting season the upper sides of the leaves are glossy and olive green. Underneath, the leaves are grayish. Each leaf has about five to seven pairs of short teeth, with a vein extending to each tooth. These lateral veins are impressed only slightly on the upper face but are very definite on the under side. They form an angle of approximately 45 degrees with the midrib.

Leaves of the cork oak remain on the tree usually for 2 or 3 years. When the tree is grown outside of its native habitat and winter temperatures fall well below freezing, the leaves turn pale brown during the cold weather. They remain on the tree until late spring when new growth appears, and then they drop.

The cork oak begins to fruit when 12 to 15 years old and bears abundantly after 25 to 30 years. Acorns during the growing season have a brilliant green color which presents an effective contrast to their light gray cupules. By September the acorns begin to mature and they slowly change color and finally become dark brown with a wax-like luster. At this stage, which occurs from October to January, the acorns drop, some with cupules attached.

The acorns are of several different shapes and may be oval, roller-shaped or elliptical with rounded ends. They vary in size: the length may be $\frac{3}{4}$ in. to 2 in.; the diameter ranges from $\frac{3}{8}$ in. to $\frac{3}{4}$ in. Average acorns number about one hundred to the pound but sixty or less of the larger acorns will equal this weight. The cupule is cone-shaped at the bottom and has slightly extending plates which terminate in lace-like clusters. The cupules extend from one-quarter to one-third the length of the acorns.

Cork formation is common in many plants and especially in trees. However, in only a few plants does the cork development attain a thickness of one or more inches. The cork oak not only produces a thick growth of cork, but, importantly, the cork may be removed periodically without affecting the vitality of the tree. No cork is visible on a 1-year-old stem, but it is discernible on older stems. The cork cambium has then been formed and has become active. It continues to produce cork during all future growing seasons. Because cork is a tissue made up of dead cells, the tissue stretches as the stem increases in diameter and then develops fissures.

When the first growth of cork is removed from the tree, the remaining tissue exposed to the air oxidizes to a red tint. This color slowly deepens to a reddish brown and finally to a dark brown. Inside this dark brown layer the process of cork formation continues. Again, as the cork layer becomes thicker, pressure produces ridges and furrows, but they are not as deep as in the virgin cork. When the second-growth cork has reached a thickness of one or more inches, sufficient to make its removal commercially profitable, it may be taken off the tree. This cycle can be repeated as long as the tree lives.

A transverse section of cork shows the presence of a number of layers which are separated by dark lines or zones. These layers denote the year-by-year formation of the cork. By counting these annual rings the age of a piece of cork can be determined. The cork cells produced in the fall of the year have thicker walls, dark tissue and are very close together. This formation develops in cork, as in wood, towards the end of the season when growth is slow.[15] As a general rule annual layers are thicker at the outside of a piece of cork and gradually diminish in magnitude towards the inside. This results from the fact the cells of the outer layer which develop first have little to confine them and they grow without restraint; layers away from the outside tend to be compressed. However, exceptions to this generalization are found, for wider layers are formed in years that are favorable for growth than are produced in unseasonable years.

CULTURE AND HARVEST

Fire is the ever-present enemy of all forests. Undergrowth and dead wood furnish abundant material for forest fires. By keeping the cork forests free of this unneeded and hazardous material damage by fire has been greatly reduced. At the same time young cork trees have grown faster and the old cork oaks are surviving longer in the clean, cultivated forests. Properly done in the right seasons this work has proven not to be too costly. The increased growth combined with the ease of getting to the trees during the stripping period helps the cultivated forest pay for itself.

The greater part of the commercial cork forests are of natural origin. Cork forests have been growing for centuries, the old dead trees being replaced by volunteer trees. As long as the available supply of cork was sufficient to meet demands there was no urge for additional planting. The important work of propagation was left entirely to nature and fortunately was carried on very satisfactorily. However, in the last 60 years, as the industrial uses of cork continued to increase, considerable attention has been given to developing new cork areas. This work has been carried out largely by the governments of the various cork-producing countries, but private plantings also have been made. In addition to scientific reforestation the established cork forests have received much needed care and attention.

Good forestry practice begins with proper attention to the existing trees, and today the cork forests are under excellent management. With the fire hazards reduced to a minimum by good maintenance, efforts have been directed toward improving and preserving the trees individually. The correct method of pruning cork trees has been emphasized. Cutting away of undesirable branches and properly trimming others, to enable the tree to produce more and better cork, have received special study. Illustrated bulletins showing what growth should be removed and the correct method for cutting these branches close to the remaining limbs have been distributed widely. This has resulted in healthier, more vigorous trees and a higher yield of cork.

Along with improvements in the technique of pruning have come advances in the very important operation of stripping the trees. Emphasis on this phase of cork production has enabled the owners to obtain their cork with less damage to the tree. This extra care has provided dividends of both increased yields in subsequent strippings and some improvement in the quality of the cork.

Planned and scientific reforestation is practiced generally today by the owners of cork forests. Improved planting techniques are employed in establishing new cork areas. Several methods are used for planting cork trees. Seedlings are transplanted sometimes, but the direct planting of acorns is the recommended procedure.

A report on reforestation by Gois is given in a recent issue of *Junta Nacional da Cortica*. From this article we quote:

As regards artificial arborization a considerable amount has been affected in this country and replantations of several hundred hectares are frequently found. Although some cork oak tree plantations do exist with seedlings obtained from nurseries or by transplanting volunteer trees from other localities, generally artificial replanting is carried out by seeds.[16]

The author reviews reforestation from nursery-grown seedlings, volunteer trees and direct seeding. He discusses several methods of planting acorns and points out direct seeding is the most economical and successful method of planting cork trees.

The owners of cork forests are conscious of the value of superior cork oaks and are making efforts to improve the tree genetically. From an abstract of an article by J. V. Natividade we quote:

> In view of the importance of the cork oak to the Portuguese economy, considerable emphasis is being placed at the present time on the selection and clonal propagation of plus trees. Owing to the heterozygous nature of the species and the diversity of types found throughout the country, considerable progress has been achieved in improving the quality of the cork and increasing the rate of growth of the tree. Increased yields of acorns, which are used for fodder, a reduction in the incidence of alternate bearing and improved resistance to diseases and insect pests have also been obtained by straightforward selection. Intraspecific and interspecific crosses are now to be effected to explore the possibilities of exploiting hybrid vigour and experiments aimed at inducing favorable mutations will be carried out.[17]

Only a small percentage of the cork acorns produced are needed for propagation. The bulk of each year's crop is used for feeding hogs. In the large forests, hogs graze through the areas during the period the acorns are falling. This extends over 6 or 8 weeks. The charge for the acorns varies but usually is based on the weight increase shown by the hogs. The owner weighs his hogs before and after turning them into the cork forest and the gain in weight determines the total charge. The total quantity of cork acorns consumed as hog food is quite large. It has been estimated that approximately 200,000 tons of cork acorns are fed to hogs every year in Portugal alone.[18] A careful check has estimated that a bushel of cork acorns, or about 70 pounds, will put 6.6 pounds of weight on a hog.[19] This means that cork acorns in Portugal are annually converted into some 18,000 tons of pork.

When the cork tree is 20 years old or 9 inches in diameter, the cork bark may be stripped from the trunk of the tree. This operation when properly carried out does not harm the tree, and cork begins to grow again at once. The new cork, known in the trade as reproduction cork, grows much faster than the original or "virgin" cork, and the tree is ready

(Courtesy, Crown Cork & Seal Co.)

This piece of cork has first growth, virgin cork, at the top and second growth below.

for stripping again in 8 or 10 years. This process continues throughout the life of the tree. With the third and subsequent stripping high quality cork that meets the most exacting requirements of industry is obtained.

Cork trees are stripped in the summer when the foliage is new and the tree is growing. The sap should be flowing freely as this causes the cork bark to separate readily from the tree. No sap flows through the cork. The cells are dead and their walls are highly resistant to the passage of water. Rain is infrequent during the summer months of the cork-producing areas, but a good rain stimulates the flow of sap and this facilitates the removal of the cork. June and July are the usual cork stripping months, but when necessary the period can be extended by including a part of May or a part of August or parts of both.

The stripping operation is carried out by making circular cuts at the base of the tree and just below the first branches. Then vertical cuts are made, and by utilizing the natural voids in the bark the cork is easily separated from the tree. The bark is removed in slabs as big as possible for large sections of cork bring a higher price than smaller pieces. On large trees in some forests cork is stripped, also, from a portion of the lower branches.

The actual stripping is carried out by skilful workmen who swing their stripping hatchets with just the correct force to cut through the cork and not to damage the inner tissues. Special hatchets are used for cutting the cork. The handles are wedge shaped at the open end and serve as levers for prying away the cork bark. The experienced strippers climb over the lower branches of the cork trees and wield the hatchet with speed and dexterity. Untrained laborers gather the cork and place it in piles under the tree.

The cork varies in thickness, but the minimum for profitable stripping is about 1 in. The yield per tree depends upon the size of the tree, the height to which it is stripped and the thickness of the bark. A young cork oak may produce only 35 pounds of cork, while from large trees several hundred pounds can be obtained. From an exceptionally large cork tree having a trunk 25 ft in circumference 2310 pounds of cork were obtained at one stripping. Twelve years later 2112 pounds of cork were taken from the same tree.[19] A skilled stripper can gather from 300 to 800 pounds of cork in a day. The total harvest by one workman depends on the number of trees per acre, and the yield per tree.

The stripped bark is hauled to designated central stations where further operations prepare it for baling. The cork is stacked and left to season for a few weeks. This curing period allows excess moisture to evaporate and aids in flattening the curved bark. The corkbark is then boiled. Boiling is carried out in big copper tanks, large bundles of the cork being lowered into the boiling water by means of block and tackle. Heavy weights keep the cork submerged for about 30 minutes. The boiling process removes tannins, any other water soluble-materials that might be

(*Courtesy, Crown Cork & Seal Co.*)

A bundle of cork being raised from the tank of water where it has been boiled.

present, loose dirt and extraneous matter. Also the cork is softened and the rough, hard outside portion of the cork known in the trade as "hard-back" is loosened so that it can readily be scraped off after the cork is removed from the vats. Hoe-shaped knives are employed for scraping away this outer portion, which amounts to about 2 percent of the volume of corkbark and from 15 to 20 percent of the weight. An average day's work for a man skilled in the scraping operation is said to be from 450 to 600 pounds per day.

After the cork has been boiled and scraped it is allowed to dry. The weight of the dry material now amounts to about two-thirds of the weight when stripped. The pieces are next cut, trimmed and graded.

(*Courtesy, Crown Cork & Seal Co.*)

Baling cork for shipment, after the pieces have been trimmed.

The different grades are compactly baled, each bale weighing from 150 to 200 pounds depending on the quality of the corkwood. Before shipment the bales are opened and inspected, and the corkwood is again sorted into many grades of quality and thickness. This classifying of cork is carried out by expert graders. The importance of grading can readily be realized since the economic manufacture of cork products depends upon utilizing the proper quality of cork for each process. The finest grades of cork are required for the manufacture of cork stoppers and certain types of composition cork, while less expensive cork can be used in many of the other numerous cork products.

An excellent presentation on the culture of cork trees has been written by J. V. Natividade.[20] The pruning of cork trees, the correct procedure for removing the cork and methods of reforestation are discussed.

CHAPTER III

STRUCTURE AND PHYSICAL PROPERTIES

It is quality rather than quantity that matters.

SENECA

CORK is non-fibrous and is composed of tiny cells. Under high magnification the characteristic cellular structure of cork can be seen. The cells vary in size but are very small and number about two hundred million to the cubic inch. They are filled with air and held together by a strong natural resinous binding substance.

As early as 1665 Robert Hooke published a description of cork, which he observed under the microscope, and introduced the term "cell".[21] Professor Frederic T. Lewis of Harvard has shown that the cork cell possesses fourteen sides, six of them being quadrilaterals and eight of them hexagons.[22] The presence of these fourteen-sided cells in cork is due to nature's method of giving the cells the greatest possible volume with the least amount of surface while permitting the cells to lie compactly together. Here is a typical example in nature of the observation made by Lord Kelvin that a fourteen-sided surface requires the minimum of material for covering any volume. Of course, all cork cells are not perfect tetrakaidecahedrons. Due to the rate of growth, crowding and other factors, many cork cells have less than fourteen faces. If a thin section of cork be treated to remove the cell binding material the cells will often appear under the microscope as four-sided or six-sided bodies depending upon which face is toward the lens of the instrument.

Cork possesses physical characteristics which are a direct result of its air-filled cellular structure. These qualities are given in the following paragraphs and discussed separately

COMPRESSIBILITY AND RESILIENCY

Cork is compressible and resilient and these properties have made it indispensable in numerous applications for many years. A piece of cork

Fig: I.

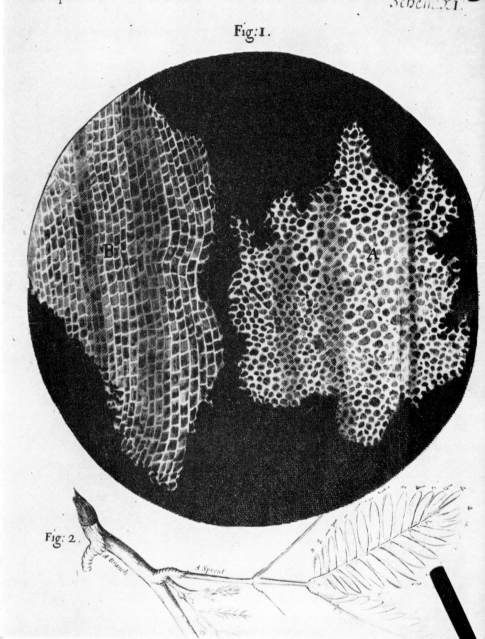

Fig: 2.

(Courtesy, Science Se

A science classic. This illustration from Robert Hooke's *Micrographia*, published in 1665, is the first known picture of what plant cells look like under the microscope. Hooke was looking at a piece of cork when he drew it.

can be reduced in thickness without showing any spreading at the sides. One-inch cubes of cork have been subjected to high pressure without any side spread. After the pressure was released the cork returned to 95 percent of the original height. When subjected to pressure some of the air in cork

(*Courtesy, Crown Cork & Seal Co.*)

Photograph of cork cells, magnified 500 times.

passes out while a portion remains trapped in the cells and is compressed. After the pressure is released, the compressed air expands and the specimen of cork returns to its original volume. Compressibility and resiliency are qualities that enable cork to give a perfect seal when used as a liner in crown bottle caps, as a stopper or gasket. In crown caps each tiny cell of the cork liner functions as an air cushion permitting the crown cap to be compressed firmly against the mouth of the container and constantly exerting a back pressure, thus making a tight and permanent seal.

Studies on the elasticity of cork have been carried out by Dart and Guth.[23] They showed cork under low compression follows Hooke's law but at higher pressures the cells collapse and the material itself is compressed.

IMPERVIOUSNESS TO WATER AND OTHER LIQUIDS

Both the air-filled cork cells and the natural resinous binder which holds them together are impervious to water. Cork is oil-resistant also, and on account of its non-capillarity, which results from its cellular structure, penetration of cork by liquids in general is extremely difficult. For this reason cork can be used to seal wine, champagne and other bottled beverages as well as innumerable solutions and liquids.

LOW SPECIFIC GRAVITY

Cork is very light, its specific gravity varying between 0.20 and 0.25. This lightness is due principally to its air-filled cellular structure. The cork cell walls and the natural cell binding material are also lightweight substances. This property of cork gives it many applications where life preservers, floats and other articles of low density, for example inner soles for shoes, are required.

LOW THERMAL CONDUCTIVITY

Air, in finely divided spaces, makes an excellent thermal insulator. In fact small air divisions are second only to a vacuum in retarding heat transfer. The tiny air-filled cells of cork are responsible for its outstanding heat insulating characteristic. Nature has provided cork with thousands of individual air spaces per cubic inch in the form of air-filled cells which greatly retard the transfer of heat at low and moderate temperatures. The thermal conductivity of cork is very low and cork is an excellent material for low temperature insulation. This property, together with the low density and moisture resistance, has given cork a leading position in the field of insulation materials. Although other types of low temperature insulation materials are now manufactured, corkboard is still preferred for many applications.

VIBRATION ABSORBENCY

The resiliency of cork has made it an important machinery isolation material. Just as pneumatic tires on an automobile absorb road shocks, the air-filled cells in cork take up vibration and reduce wear of mounted machines. Sudden pressures and jolts cause the air-filled cells to quickly compress, shock is absorbed and the vibrations are not transmitted through cork.

HIGH COEFFICIENT OF FRICTION

When a piece of cork is trimmed the cells are cut and thousands of microscopic cups are formed on the surface. In these tiny cups partial vacuums are formed when cork is drawn over or pressed against a smooth surface. This accounts for the high coefficient of friction exhibited by cork and for its suitability in many applications where a material of non-slipping character is essential.

SOUND ABSORBENCY

Cork as an acoustic material has an important place in modern building construction. Cork is employed to insulate against outside noise and to absorb sound formed within, and to prevent echoes. The cut cells on the exterior of cork provide an ideal surface for absorbing sound waves.

Thus we see that cork possesses many valuable physical properties. It is the combination of the properties of compressibility and resilience, water resistance and non-capillarity, low specific gravity, thermal insulation, machinery isolation, high coefficient of friction and sound absorption in a single material that has made cork an important natural product for over two thousand years. No other naturally occurring plant product in its raw or unmanufactured state has so many valuable physical attributes. Other materials having only one or two of these eight characteristics have become important commodities. It is these many qualities that have given cork a prominent place in the commercial world for almost a century. The possessing of these eight physical characteristics by a single substance has enabled cork to maintain its commercial importance in our present technological age.

CHAPTER IV

CHEMICAL COMPOSITION

Curiosity is one of the permanent and certain
characteristics of a vigorous mind.

SAMUEL JOHNSON

THE characteristics of cork have made it a valuable and necessary commodity. It is interesting to associate the properties of a material with its various applications, and with cork some knowledge of its properties is essential before its numerous applications can be appreciated. The chemical and physical characteristics of cork determine its uses and the chemical attributes are reviewed in the following pages.

For centuries the stability of cork has been an outstanding chemical characteristic. This fact may be due to long exposure, 8 to 12 years, in an abundance of sunlight during which the corkbark as it grows is subjected to the weathering conditions covering a range of temperatures common to the cork forest areas through rainy winters and dry summers mixed with strong winds. Under these conditions cork develops an unusual resistance to degradation by sunlight, air and moisture. The author has examined the remains of a dead cork tree which had fallen to the ground some 20 years earlier. All of the hard, woody portion of the tree had decayed and had been either washed away by rain or blown away by wind. Only the hollow, cylindrical pieces of corkbark remained and they were in an excellent state of preservation. In fact, there was no outstanding difference between this cork, which had laid on the earth for more than 20 years, and cork which had been removed from vigorous trees and stored for approximately 1 year.

This remarkable resistance to deterioration which is inherent in cork has made it suitable for many diversified applications. Clean cork of commerce is not changed in composition by contact with water, vegetable, animal or mineral oils, gasoline, numerous organic liquids, and many gases, such as carbon dioxide, hydrogen, nitrogen and air. Cork is highly resistant to fruit and vegetable acids, dilute hydrochloric and phosphoric acids, and literally thousands of chemical compounds. Its use as a stopper or closure on containers for innumerable articles of commerce attests the chemical resistance and durability of cork. No other untreated naturally occurring plant product can be used in contact with so many different substances.

However, there are certain chemicals that have a decided reaction on cork. Strong alkalies saponify the binding substance which holds the cells together and break down the cork structure. Cork is attacked, also, by the halogens. Iodine and bromine should not be kept in bottles stoppered with cork. Chlorine reacts with cork and even dilute chlorine preparations should not be kept under cork closures.

More than 150 years have passed since chemists first endeavoured to learn the composition of cork. Scattered papers have appeared from time to time but the literature on this subject is not extensive. Since the turn of the century some excellent research has been carried out on the constituents of cork. Today, while we know more about the composition of cork than at any time since its use began more than 2000 years ago, there is still much to learn.

Chemical investigations of cork were undertaken in the eighteenth century and as early as 1787 the Italian chemist Brugnatelli[24] reported he obtained suberic acid, $HOOC(CH_2)_6COOH$, by treating cork with nitric acid. Ten years later, La Grange,[25] a French chemist, repeated the work of Brugnatelli and checked the results. Suberic acid is formed by the oxidation of cork with nitric acid.

In 1807, the French chemist Chevreul[26] also obtained suberic acid from cork by the action of nitric acid. In addition he reported the presence of oxalic acid in the reaction products. While no attempt was made to determine the formula of suberic acid Chevreul pointed out its similarity to sebasic acid.

Chevreul extracted cork with alcohol and obtained a product which he thought was a wax. Accordingly he gave the name "cerine" to this product. Further study proved cerin not to be a wax. Chevreul believed he had obtained a single substance but research later on proved this product to be a mixture of two compounds.

In 1836, Boussingault[27] extracted cerin from cork and, upon purifying it from ether, obtained crystals in the form of small needles. Boussingault gave the formula $C_{32}H_{20}O$ to cerin. Dopping[28] in 1843 suggested that cerin has the formula corresponding to $C_{25}H_{20}O_3$. Siewert[29] in 1863 proposed the formula $C_{17}H_{28}O$. In 1884 Kügler[30] in his studies on cork gave the formula $C_{20}H_{32}O$ to cerin. It should be kept in mind that in all of this research the cerin samples under investigation were impure. Subsequent research showed the material to be mixture and this explains the varying results that had been reported.

(*Courtesy, Crown Cork & Seal Co.*)

Crystals of cerin, magnified 225 times.

In 1892 Friedel[31] isolated cerin and in studying the compound found it contained a carbonyl group. Thoms[32] in 1898 gave the empirical formula $C_{30}H_{50}O_2$ to cerin which evidently was a pure sample since later investigators have checked his formula.

Istrati and Ostrogovich[33] extracted cerin with alcohol, but they could not obtain a uniform product. They then proceeded to purify the material by a long series of recrystallizations from chloroform. Through this procedure they succeeded in separating the material into two substances. They gave the name *cerin* to the less soluble portion and *friedelin*, in honor of the celebrated French chemist, Friedel, to the more soluble. To cerin, which had a melting point of 234–234.5° centigrade they gave the formula $C_{27}H_{44}O_2$. Friedelin, which melted at 263–263.5°, was reported to correspond to the formulas $C_{43}H_{70}O_2$ or $C_{21}H_{34}O$.

Drake and his co-workers have carried out a series of excellent studies on cerin and friedelin. Drake and Jacobsen[34] showed the empirical formula of cerin, which they found to melt at 247–251°, to be $C_{30}H_{50}O_2$

and that of friedelin, which has a melting point of 255–261°, to be $C_{30}H_{50}C$. They further showed that both cerin and friedelin could be reduced to the same hydrocarbon, $C_{30}H_{52}$. Drake and Shrader[35] prepared functional derivatives of cerin and friedelin which showed cerin to be an hydroxyketone and friedelin to be a ketone. Drake and Campbell[36] conducted oxidative degradation studies on friedelin and showed the structure $CHCOCH_2$—to be present in the friedelin molecule. In further studies on friedelin Drake and Haskins[37] dehydrogenated the molecule and showed cerin and friedelin should be classed with the triterpenoids. Drake and Wolfe[38] oxidized friedelin to friedonic acid and made further studies on the presence of a carbonyl group in friedelin.

Corey and Ursprung[39] in a series of experiments studied the structure of friedelin. They proved the location of oxygen on the third carbon and also determined the positions of the eight methyl groups in the molecule. They showed cerin to be 2 beta-hydroxylfriedelin.

Approximately 3 percent of cork by weight is cerin and friedelin. Kügler[30] reported he obtained 2.9 percent of cerin, which has been shown to be a mixture of cerin and friedelin. Zemplen[40] reported he obtained 3 grams of cerin and friedelin when he extracted 100 grams of cork with alcohol.

It was von Hohnel[41] who in 1877 first pointed out the presence of acid substances in cork. He showed how cork could be saponified by the action of an alkali in manner similar to the saponification of esters.

Kügler[30] confirmed these observations of Hohnel and isolated acids from cork. One of these acids he called phellonic acid. Kügler found phellonic acid when purified to melt at 96° and from his analysis he assigned the formula $C_{22}H_{42}O_3$.

A few years later Gilson[42] treated cork with a 3 percent alcoholic solution of potassium hydroxide and obtained phellonic acid and along with it two additional acids. Gilson's phellonic acid melted at 95–96° when crystallized from chloroform. The new acids isolated from cork were designated as suberinic acid to which Gilson gave the formula $C_{17}H_{30}O_3$ and phloionic acid to which Gilson assigned the formula $C_{11}H_{21}O_4$.

M. von Schmidt[43] in 1904 studied the characteristics of phellonic acid and agreed with Kügler's empirical formula. He showed phellonic acid to be a saturated hydroxy acid and he believed it to have a cyclic structure. Von Schmidt also isolated another acid which he called phellogenic acid and to which he assigned the formula $C_{21}H_{40}O_4$.

In 1916 Scurti and Tommasi[44] made additional studies on phellonic acid and believed it to be alpha-hydroxybehenic acid, $CH_3(CH_2)_{19}$-CHOHCOOH. They also carried out research on the other acids of cork but did not propose formulas.

Zetsche and Rosenthal[45] and Zetsche, Cholatnikov and Scherz[46] in their work on the acids of cork agreed that phellonic acid is alpha-hydroxybehenic acid. Zetsche and Sonderegger[47] carried out an extensive study of cork fatty acids. They separated the acids in the form of sodium salts, having discovered that the sodium salt of each acid has a characteristic OH ion concentration at which it will precipitate. Using this procedure they isolated phloionic acid which melted at 121° and another acid which gave a melting point of 99–100°. Zetsche and Bähler[48] further purified phloionic acid by converting it to the potassium salt, refluxing in a 1 to 3 mixture of benzene–alcohol, reconverting to the acid and recrystallizing several times. The phloionic acid thus purified melted at 123.5–124.5° and was shown to be eicosanedicarboxylic acid, $C_{18}H_{34}O_6$. They also obtained phloionolic acid from cork which they found to melt at 61°. Zetsche and Weber[49] studied the structures of phloionic and phloionolic acids. Since phloionic acid was oxidized to nonalic acid they gave it the formula $HOOC(CH_2)_7(CHOH)_2(CH_2)_7$-COOH. To phloionolic acid they assigned the formula $HOCH_2$-$(CHOH)_2(CH_2)_7COOH$. Also, they pointed out that phellonic, phloionic and phloionolic acids are not optically active.

In 1941 Drake, Carhart and Mozingo[50] showed that phellonic acid was not alpha-hydroxybehenic acid but contained twenty-four carbon atoms. They further showed the hydroxy group was not on the alpha carbon atom. By preparing 1, 20-eicosanedicarboxylic acid from the alkaline fusion and oxidation of phellonic acid, they showed the latter to be 22-hydroxytetracosanoic acid.

Erlenmeyer and Müller[51] in a publication about phellonic acid in 1945 checked the work of Drake, Carhart and Mozingo and also found this acid to be 22-hydroxytetracosanoic acid.

In 1950 Guillemonat and Strich[52] carried out research on phellonic acid and reported it to have the structure of omega-hydroxybehenic acid of the formula $HO-CH_2-(CH_2)_{20}COOH$. Ribas and Curbera[53] prepared urea derivatives of phellonic acid and acetylated phellonic acid. From the percentages of the urea derivatives formed they found phellonic acid to conform to the formula for omega-hydroxybehenic acid.

Jensen[54] in 1950 conducted independent research and reported phellonic acid to conform to the structure of omega-hydroxybehenic acid.

Cork contains cellulose and as early as 1843 Dopping[28] considered the insoluble portion which separated when cork was treated with nitric acid to be cellulose without specific identification. Mulder[55] in 1844 stated cork does not contain cellulose. Payen,[56] Wiesner[57] and Haberland[58] obtained reactions with the residue left after saponifying the cork acids which indicated the presence of cellulose.

Von Hohnel[41] stated cellulose is present in cork and Fremy and Urbain[59] believed cork to contain about 12 percent cellulose but neither of these researchers tells how the presence of cellulose was indicated. Kügler[30] reported cork to contain 22 percent cellulose, but gave no proof of its presence. Gilson[42] believed the presence of cellulose in cork was shown by the coloration obtained with zinc chloroiodide. Van Wiessling[60] denied the presence of cellulose in cork.

In spite of these claims and denials regarding the presence of cellulose in cork nothing definite upon which to base a strong opinion had been presented. In 1913 Zemplen[40] proved the presence of a carbohydrate that is similar to cellulose but not identical. In 1923 Karrer, Peyer and Zega[61] showed conclusively that cellulose is present in cork. They also expressed their belief that other carbohydrates are present in cork in addition to cellulose.

Zetsche and Rosenthal[45] in 1927 reported from 2 to 2.5 percent of cellulose in raw cork. When cork is treated with hydrogen peroxide, "oxy-cork" results and in this form shows from 3.3 to 4.0 percent cellulose.

In 1928 Zetsche, Cholatnikov and Scherz[46] showed that cellulose exists free in cork and is not combined with other cork constituents. In 1935 Madinaveitia[62] studied cork cellulose and reported 8 percent in virgin cork and 10 percent in better grades.

Stockar[63] in 1948 cleared the situation concerning cellulose in cork. He dissolved it in Schweitzer's reagent, precipitated and hydrolyzed the recovered cellulose. Then he prepared the osazone of the glucose formed. In addition Stockar prepared the triacetate and the trinitrate derivatives of the cellulose from cork.

Cork as it comes from the trees contains tannins. The greater portion of the tannins are removed during the water boiling of the freshly stripped cork. The remaining tannins may be extracted with the usual tannin solvents. Even in the very best grades of cork traces of a reddish-brown powder can be found. This substance is composed of compounds called phlobaphenes. They are complex substances and their chemical behavior is closely related to that of the tannins. Phlobaphenes occur in nature along with tannins and according to Haas and Hill[64] are anhydrides of tannins.

Kügler[30] extracted cork with alcohol and obtained 5.6 percent of a mixture of tannins and phlobaphenes. Zemplen[40] obtained 7.5 percent of tanning matter from cork that had not been extracted exhaustively.

Glycerine has been found in cork and its presence was first announced by Kügler in 1884.[30] Kügler found 2.65 percent glycerine and proved its presence by preparing nitroglycerine. Gilson[42] a few years later in 1890 found glycerine in the aqueous liquid after saponifying cork. Gilson proved the presence of glycerine by preparing the tribenzoate derivative. In 1904 Schmidt[43] stated cork does not contain glycerine. Zetsche and Rosenthal in 1927[45] believed that cork in its natural condition as well as "oxy-cork" does not contain glycerine.

In view of these differences of opinion Ribas and Blasco in 1940[65] conducted research on cork to determine if glycerine is present. They found glycerine present to the extent of 6 to 7 percent. Cork which had been extracted for 5 hours with water, alcohol, ether and chloroform contained the same quantity of glycerine as cork which had not been submitted to any kind of treatment. They obtained glycerine when cork was saponified and accordingly decided that the glycerine in cork is a part of a molecule which is insoluble in water and fat solvents. They prepared the tribenzoate, the tri-para-nitrobenzoate, the tri-alpha-napthylurathane and the tri-phenylurathane derivatives of glycerine from cork and pure glycerine.

Stockar in 1948[63] obtained glycerine from cork by extracting with methanol for 150 hours. He identified the glycerine by preparing the benzoate and para-nitrobenzoate derivatives.

In their investigation of the composition of cork Zetsche and Luscher[66] obtained a wax for which they give the following composition:

Arachic Acid	1.00 percent
Cerotic Acid	1.00 percent
Oxyarachic Acid	1.50 percent
Phellonic Acid	0.50 percent
Oleic Acid	1.00 percent
Linoleic	1.50 percent
Friedelin and Cerin	19.00 percent
$C_{30}H_{48}O_3$ (acid)	2.00 percent

$C_{24}H_{42}O_2$ (alcohol)	2.10 percent
Phytosterol	0.60 percent
Mixed Sterols	10.00 percent

TOTAL	40.20

They do not state the nature of the remaining 59.80 percent. Warth[67] discusses the wax and other constituents of cork.

The composition of cork has been investigated by extractions. These studies generally have consisted of extractions with solvents, extractions involving chemical action and examination of the residue. The materials used and the treatment of cork follows conventional methods.

1. Solvents

(a) *Hot water.* Finely divided cork is held in boiling water for a period of 30 minutes. The water removes tannins and other plant compounds. This extract may contain as high as 9 percent of the cork.

(b) *Organic solvents.* Alcohol, chloroform, benzene, esters and other solvents will remove cerin, friedelin, waxes and any uncombined acids. As high as 10 percent of the cork may be extracted with organic solvents.

2. Chemical action with alcoholic potassium hydroxide removes fatty acids and lignin. By such treatment as much as 50 percent of the cork may be removed.

3. The residue, which consists of materials insoluble in water and organic solvents and not rendered soluble by mild chemical treatment, contains cellulose and related compounds.

Chemical analyses of cork reported by several investigators vary widely. One of the earliest was carried out by the German chemist, Kügler, in 1844.[30] His results are:

Water	5.00 percent
Solvent Extraction	19.00 percent
Alcoholic KOH	32.65 percent
Water Extract of Residue	8.00 percent
Cellulose	22.00 percent
Lignin	12.00 percent*

TOTAL	98.65 percent

* By calculation wood contains cellulose 64 percent and lignin 36 percent.

In 1942 Guillemonat,[68] a French chemist, reported the organic constituents of cork as follows:

1. Extracted with Solvents   19 percent
2. Removed by Chemical Action   53 percent
3. Residue   27 percent

Cork is principally an organic material and the ash content of a good grade of cork is relatively low. The quantity of ash from cork has been reported as follows:

RESEARCHER	YEAR	PERCENT	
Zemplen	1913	4.12	[40]
Kügler	1884	0.54 to 0.64	[30]
Barcelo	1939	2.1 to 2.6	[69]

The wide range in the percentages of ash found may be due, in part, to the type of sample used and its source. In the ash were found potassium, sodium, magnesium, calcium, aluminium, iron, manganese, barium and strontium. Calcium and magnesium were present to a greater extent than the other elements.

COMMERCIAL ASPECTS

In Portugal the National Center of Scientific Research has patented processes for obtaining products from cork. A hard wax equal to 15 percent by weight of the cork used and melting from 80° to 90°C is obtained by saponifying cork. It is stated the wax may be used as a substitute for carnauba wax. A factory was set up in Algiers in 1946 and another in Portugal in 1951.

The cork is treated for 3 hours at 103°C with a 30 percent NaOH solution. Since the sodium salts are soluble the mass of filtrate is acidified to free the acids. The liberated acids are then separated by filtration and pressed dry. They are next solvent-extracted in order to further purify them. The solvent is distilled and a dark mass of waxy material equal to 45 percent of the weight of the cork is obtained. Evidently some colloidal matter is carried along with the acids and further purification with solvents gives a fraction of clear wax melting from 59° to 64°C, equivalent to 19 percent yield, and a very dark fraction melting from 58° to 55°, equivalent to 16 percent.

Soaps made with the fatty acids produce little lather but are good detergents. When heated the mixture of fatty acids undergoes reaction and produces a resinous-like gum. This resinous gum is reported to be useful for making varnishes that are employed in lining containers for beer and fruit juices.

CHAPTER V

MANUFACTURE OF NATURAL CORK ARTICLES

A connection frequently exists between physical and
chemical properties and in many cases recourse must
be had to both for an explanation of a phenomenon
to which they may each contribute.

C. L. BERTHOLLET

ONE of the oldest and most widely known uses of cork is in the manufacture of bottle stoppers. The varied physical properties of cork and its
chemical stability make it an ideal material for bottle closures. When a
cork stopper is pushed into the neck of a bottle the cork is compressed and
because cork is resilient it constantly exerts a pressure against the inside of
the bottle neck. The high coefficient of friction of cork prevents stoppers
from becoming loose and slipping out. It is in this way that cork makes a
tight and permanent seal.

It is difficult to estimate accurately the quantity of cork stoppers manufactured annually. The number runs into large figures and the value into
millions of dollars. Cork stoppers are made in a wide range of sizes and
shapes to fit the necks of small glass vials, the wide openings of large jars
and the numerous designs of commercial bottles. The sizes of cork stoppers
are listed as 1 to 26 but they are made larger for special use. They are
made short, long and regular. Some have straight sides while others are
tapered. Very large corks are laminated, that is, made from several pieces
bonded together.

The cork stopper industry naturally originated in Europe. For
centuries pieces of cork were cut and trimmed to fit the openings in jars
and vases. The need for stoppers before the fifteenth century was very
limited. After the invention of the glass bottle the demand for cork
stoppers increased and by 1760 the cork industry, of which cork stoppers
was the principal product, had made its beginning.

Originally cork stoppers were made entirely by hand and even today there are a limited number of handmade cork stoppers produced in Europe. The process is simple but the actual cutting and trimming of the cork to make stoppers is carried out by skilled craftsmen. Selected cork-bark is first cut into narrow strips and then the strips are divided into small squares. The size of the stopper that is to be made determines the thickness of the bark selected and the dimensions of the squares. Using a sharp knife the workman turns the cork cube rapidly and in a very short time a stopper is made. The hand cut "corks" are smooth and remarkably uniform in dimensions. This is all the more interesting when the fact that a good workman can average three handmade corks every minute is considered.

As the use of cork stoppers increased the need for machinery to make the corks became more and more urgent. About 1805 a patent was granted to Sarah Thompson in England[70] on a machine operated by hand, steam, horse or other power for the manufacture of cork stoppers. This was a step that greatly speeded up the manufacture of corks and resulted in lower prices with increased demand. The original machine was a far cry from the equipment in a modern factory today, but our present high speed cork-manufacturing machines are the result of improvements and developments over a period of some 150 years.

The manufacture of corks begins with the proper selection of high quality cork. Slabs of the desired thickness are placed in a steam chamber for a period of 20 minutes or more. Steam softens the cork and makes it pliable and easy to cut. For reasons of economy exhaust steam is usually employed in this operation. After the cork has been softened with steam the slabs are cut into strips. The width of the strips is equal to the length of the stoppers to be manufactured for the corks are punched perpendicular to the pores of the bark. The strips of cork are now fed against rapidly revolving punches which cut out the stoppers. This operation may be by hand or automatic machine.

Corks prepared in this way have straight sides and many are used in this form, particularly for sealing wine. For general use cork stoppers are made in the tapered form. This is accomplished by feeding straight corks on to an inclined conveyor which carries them against a rapidly revolving circular knife. The conveyor also causes the corks to revolve and they emerge from this operation in the tapered form.

The corks, both straight and tapered, are then washed, bleached and sterilized. This process is carried out in large tubs, the light corks being forced under water by large revolving wooden paddles. As the paddles rotate the light corks rush to the surface only to be submerged again by other paddles. This process is remarkably efficient, the corks continually being pushed into the water and bobbing up to the surface. They are then dried in large centrifugal driers. This completes the manufacture of some stoppers but others go through additional operations, such as marking to indicate name or brand, paraffining, or special shaping.

The dry cork stoppers are now ready for sorting. Although the cork-bark used was carefully selected, the stoppers punched from this cork will vary greatly in quality and must be sorted. The assorting is carried out by trained workers, the best of whom can sort about 35,000 corks in a day. While no two corks are identical, for practical purposes they generally are placed in one of the following groups[70]:

GRADES OF CORK STOPPERS

Tapered Corks	Wine Corks	Straight Corks
Extra Select	Extra Firsts	A Quality
A Quality	Firsts	B Quality
Select	Extra Seconds	B^2 Quality
B Quality	Seconds	C Quality
XXXX	Extra Thirds	D Quality
Commercial XXXX	Thirds	E Quality
C Quality	Extra Fourths	
XXX	Fourths	Jar Corks
XX	Fifths	XXX
X		XX
Common		X

A limited number of very large corks having a diameter greater than the thickest corkbark are needed. These are made in one of two ways. The corkbark is prepared in the usual way but the cork is punched parallel to the pores of the bark. In this way very large stoppers can be made. Often they are impregnated with paraffin or a similar material. These are known as jar or specie corks and usually range from $\frac{1}{2}$ in. to $\frac{3}{4}$ in. in thickness. Sometimes corks are cut from several pieces of trimmed corkbark bonded together with an insoluble adhesive. In this way large corks for special use can be produced. They are known as laminated corks and are manufactured in several grades.

Sealing liners for crown caps is another important application for natural cork. For this product large pieces of clean corkbark free from imperfections are selected by expert inspectors. The cork must be of high

D

quality possessing fine texture and free of hard points, discolorations and excessive pores. The corkbark is steamed for about 30 minutes in exhaust steam. Following the steaming the cork is placed in a reposing room where it is kept for two or more weeks. The reposing room is warm and moist and aging in this room for several weeks properly conditions the cork for slicing.

When the cork is taken from this conditioning room it is trimmed to the required width by the slicing machine. The soft, pliable pieces of cork then are pressed on to a board through which short nails project. The rough outside of the corkbark is against the board and the nails pierce this layer which has been softened by steam and moisture. The board and nails hold the irregularly shaped pieces of cork bark flat and rigid, which greatly facilitates the slicing operation.

The steam-conditioned corkbark, firmly held on a supporting board, is now slowly fed into a slicing machine. The inner side of the corkbark, that is the part that was next to the tree, is sliced off and discarded. This portion of the cork is known in the trade as the "belly" and is suitable only for grinding purposes. The slicing is effected by a large, sharp circular steel blade which revolves at high speed. The cork is fed against the cutting blade, which can be set to give the desired thickness. Each piece of cork is passed through the slicer and trimmed several times until a smooth and uniform surface is obtained. Then the machine is set to make sheets of the correct thickness, which is approximately one-tenth of an inch. The cork slab is sliced as long as it yields good sheets. The piece remaining on the board varies in thickness from $\frac{1}{4}$ in. to $\frac{1}{2}$ in. It is separated from the board and put aside to be used for grinding.

After the slicing operation several sheets of the cork are held together firmly and fed, either manually or mechanically, against a rapidly revolving punch and the crown liners are cut out. The natural cork discs, as they are called, are then washed and sterilized. The discs are carefully sorted into several grades. Most of the natural cork crown liners are produced in Spain and Portugal. After reaching factories in the United States, and other countries, the discs are again assorted and may be processed further. They are then ready to be assembled in crown bottle caps.

In recent years a method has been developed for impregnating natural cork discs with an odorless, tasteless filler. By this process all voids and pores in the natural cork are filled and perfect sealing liners for crowns are produced. Crowns with sealing liners of natural cork treated by this process are extensively used in Europe to seal all types of pressure beverages.

Natural cork liners are assembled into crowns by automatic assembly machines. The crown caps and cork liners are conveyed to separate hoppers from which they are brought together on the assembly machine. Just before they meet, a suitable adhesive is mechanically placed inside the crown cap. Then the cork liner automatically comes into place and is pressed down firmly into the crown. As the assembled crowns leave the machine they move along on a conveyor belt where once more they pass under the watchful eyes of trained inspectors.

For centuries cork has been an essential material for shipping and navigation. It was employed by the early Greeks and Romans for floats on their fishing nets and later was used as a barricade on piers. Its resistance to penetration by water and low specific gravity are properties which make cork very satisfactory and dependable in life preservers, buoys and fishing net floats. Natural cork is employed in the manufacture of these marine articles.

The cork life preserver is known also as a life jacket and a lifebelt. Federal Government regulations specify that an adult size life preserver shall contain a minimum of $5\frac{1}{2}$ pounds of cork. The cork must be dry and of good quality. The canvas covers are made first. Then the cork is carefully cut and trimmed to fit accurately into the pockets. Sometimes two or more pieces of cork are skewered together and shaped to fit the canvas pockets. After the cork is in place the pockets are strongly sewed. Of course, the canvas and all details of the life preserver must meet the rigid requirements of Government standards.

Life preservers are made on scientific principles. Centuries ago Archimedes discovered that an object or person when wholly or partially immersed in water suffers a loss in weight equal to the weight of the water displaced. The average human being when completely submerged in water weighs approximately one-tenth as much as in air. Government specifications require that an adult's life preserver must support a weight of 20 pounds of iron in water which is equivalent to keeping afloat a human being weighing about 200 pounds. Smaller life preservers are made for children. These require approximately 3 pounds of cork and must support 10 pounds of iron in water.

Ring buoys also must meet Government specifications. They are made in various sizes but the most generally used has an outside diameter of 30 inches and is Government approved. The inside diameter is 17 inches

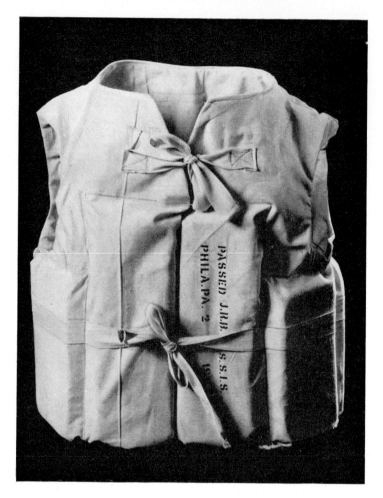

(*Courtesy, Cork Institute of America*)

A life jacket filled with cork.

which allows 6½ inches for the cork ring and cover. Ring buoys are made by shaping and fitting pieces of cork into a ring-shaped mold. An adhesive is spread between the pieces and the top is placed on the mold, compressing the cork as it is forced down, and made fast with clamps. The mold is then transferred to an oven where heat cures the adhesive. Afterward, the mold is cooled and the cork ring removed. The specially cut canvas cover is then placed about the cork buoy and strongly sewed. Finally the rope is attached completing the buoy.

There are many uses of natural cork which are more or less familiar to everyone. Cork is used in the production of sporting goods. The finest grade of baseballs have cork centers. Fishing rod handles and bobbers for fishing lines are made of cork. Hunters use duck decoys of cork and beach sandals are made with soles of natural cork. Whistles often contain small cork balls.

(*Courtesy, Crown Cork & Seal Co.*)
Many useful and decorative articles are prepared by hand carving natural cork.

Cork liners are used in the caps of containers of many toilet articles. For certain uses corks have wooden tops upon which a trade mark may be embossed. Cork rings serve to reinforce wood spigots in kegs. Fishermen employ cork floats for their seines and nets and large mooring buoys are made of cork. Cork floats are used for gasoline gauges. Handles of tools and penholder tips are made of natural cork. Cork is cut into sheets as thin as tissue paper and is used in the manufacture of cork tip cigarettes. Insoles for shoes are made of cork and cork is used to build up shoes for the lame.

In the cork-producing countries many objects of art are made of natural cork. Intricately hand carved jewelry boxes, picture frames and other ornamental items are made by skilled craftsmen.

While there are many other applications of natural cork, these are some of the most important and will serve to show the extensive use of this interesting natural product. Natural cork products cost relatively much less today than 50 years ago because of modern methods of utilizing the trimmings and other pieces of cork that formerly constituted a huge amount of waste. This portion of corkwood is now ground and purified and used in manufacturing many types of composition cork.

CHAPTER VI

COMPOSITION CORK

Experiment is the interpreter of nature. Experiments
never deceive. We must consult experiments,
varying the circumstance, until we have deduced
general rules, for experiment alone can furnish
reliable rules.

LEONARDO DA VINCI

THE cork industry developed slowly during the nineteenth century.
Progress was made but the applications of cork were limited to the
natural product. Then in the eighteen-nineties two outstanding inventions
sparked the growing cork industry.

The invention of corkboard insulation through the baking process by
John Smith in 1891 and the invention of the crown cork by William
Painter in 1892 resulted in a marked expansion of the cork industry
during the next 40 years. Smith's process for treating cork formed the
basis for the present corkboard insulation industry. This large and
important part of the cork industry is covered in Chapter VII. Natural
cork liners were used in the crown cork when it was first invented. As its
use became more widespread a less expensive cork sealing liner was
needed. Composition cork resulted and the efficient McManus process
gave this new form of cork extensive use.

As the use of cork stoppers and other natural cork products grew and
expanded a serious problem developed. Since only the very best cork was
suitable for these products a large and growing demand was placed upon
the high quality grades of natural cork. This resulted in the accumulation
of a large quantity of trimmings, known in the trade as waste or by-
product cork, for which there was no principal use. Added to this was
the scrap from broken pieces of cork and thin bark of superior grade.
The problem of economically utilizing this waste was a pressing and
growing one. All of this by-product cork was of excellent quality and
there being no steady outlet for the enormous quantity of trimmings

and small pieces of high grade cork which was accumulating rapidly the situation became more and more acute. It was imperative that a use for this scrap cork be developed.

Some of this scrap was ground and screened. It found a limited use as a packing material. Being light and waterproof the granulated cork made a suitable material to protect grapes while in transit. Some was used in packing glass, crockery, and other fragile articles. However, these small

(*Courtesy, Crown Cork & Seal Co.*)

Sampling a bale of grinding cork for laboratory testing.

miscellaneous applications did not appreciably reduce the mounting stacks of scrap cork.

Efforts to put this material to commercial use resulted in attempts to bond granulated cork with a suitable adhesive and make a compounded cork or composition cork. Experiments along this line were made as early as 1897. The task was not a simple one. The early types of composition cork were made on a small scale and, while having many meritorious features, lacked the qualities essential for general commercial production. A usable composition cork had to be strong and flexible. It must be resilient, waterproof and resistant to penetration by many liquids. More-over, when employed as a closure sealing liner for foods and beverages, the composition cork had to be odorless, tasteless and free of any toxic ingredient. The then well-known glues and adhesives for binding paper and wood were not satisfactory. The synthetic adhesives available at that time were limited in number and not suitable. In the face of such rigid requirements the solution of the problem was not easy. Certainly the answer was to be found only by patient and diligent research.

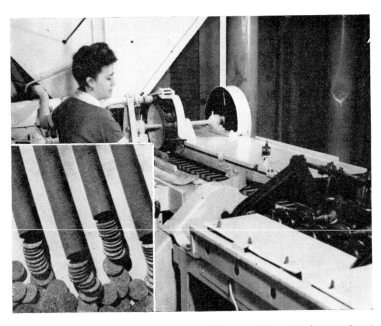

(*Courtesy, Crown Cork & Seal Co.*)

Composition cork rods are cut into discs which are used as sealing liners in beverage crown caps.

During the early years of this century the problem of developing a satisfactory composition cork was of foremost importance in the cork industry. Hundreds of experiments were carried out and the weak features of each test sample thoroughly studied. Skill and perseverance, as in all such problems, finally won and in 1909 Charles E. McManus invented for the closure industry a satisfactory composition cork for crown cap liners. McManus began commercial production of his com-position cork at once. Just how good this invention was can be shown by the continuous and expanding use of the fundamental features of this composition cork invention during the past 50 years.

Following this development the use of composition cork expanded rapidly. In addition to extensive use in the beverage fields, composition cork became an important material for manufacturing gaskets for many applications. Composition cork gaskets began to be used in automobiles, trucks, household equipment and appliances, motors, and for numerous applications where oil or water are to be sealed in and air and water are to be sealed out. In addition, the uses of this new product extended into many other fields. Shoe inner soles, polishing wheels, friction rolls, cap liners for toilet preparations, printing press blankets, decorative novelties and numerous other items were added to the list of composition cork articles.

The invention of composition cork has had far-reaching influences on the cork industry. Before its development the applications of cork were restricted by cost and many other factors. Now cork could be obtained at reasonable prices, in varying degrees of compressibility, in a wide range of densities and in large sheets or in rolls. Therefore, composition cork has become available for many industries for which natural cork was not suitable. Composition cork might well be called the complement of natural cork. While the manufactured product has in many instances replaced the natural article, at the same time composition cork has supplemented the applications of natural cork and widened the field which cork serves. In fact, the applications of composition cork today are so extensive and multitudinous that almost everyone, whether he knows it or not, depends upon cork for some important service, either directly or indirectly, every day.

The manufacture and use of composition cork constitutes one of the largest and most important phases of the cork industry. Small pieces of high quality corkwood no longer accumulate in the form of waste. Trimmings, scrap and other small pieces are ground and screened into various sizes. Only cork of the best quality can be used for this important part of cork manufacturing and the methods of granulating and preparing the cork remove all traces of any impurities that might be present.

Composition cork is manufactured by binding together clean soft granules of cork with a suitable adhesive. The adhesive is applied in such a manner that it forms only a very thin film of coating about each cork particle. Therefore, it is evident that composition cork consists mainly of natural cork. The photomicrograph of natural cork (page 21) showed the cork cells held together by a natural resinous adhesive. Composition cork differs from natural cork only in that a portion of the binding agent is artificial.

By using different adhesives many types of composition cork can be prepared and the ideal composition can be employed for a given purpose. Some composition cork gaskets are used for sealing glass and must be soft. Inner soles for shoes are tough and flexible, while polishing wheels are manufactured dense and hard.

Composition cork possesses substantially the same physical characteristics as natural cork and its chemical properties correspond closely to those of the natural material. Each cork particle, which is composed of thousands of tiny air-filled cells held together by the natural cork adhesive, is soft, compressible and resilient. The artificial adhesives employed are resilient, tough and durable. Composition cork is manufactured strong and flexible and it has good chemical resistance and stability.

The manufacture of composition cork really begins in the cork-producing countries. There the select grades of cork waste are baled for shipment. The baled cork is brought to the United States in large freight boats. The bales vary in weight from about 150 to 200 pounds. To maintain proper ballast much of the cork is piled on the ship's deck and heavier, denser freight is loaded into the ship's hold. Important cork-receiving ports in this country are located on the eastern seaboard.

Different ports require somewhat different methods of unloading a cargo of cork. In most places freight car tracks extend out on the piers and large derricks are employed to transfer the bales of cork from the boats to railroad cars. The cars carry the cork to warehouses or to storage sheds of the factory where it is to be processed. During this last transfer the bales are assorted and classified into groups. Cork waste produced in the United States as a by-product from cork stopper manufacturing is also used for composition cork.

From the storage sheds the bales of cork are taken to the grinding plant. As each bale is opened, the cork is passed on a conveyor to the breaker. Here, in this machine, the cork is broken into small pieces. In this step some of the hard, woody outside, which is known in the trade as "hardback", is crushed and removed by the breaking. The broken pieces of cork are washed to remove any loosely adhering particles. However, it is not necessary to wash all grades of cork. The washed cork is passed through a drier and then conveyed to a grinding mill which further reduces the size of the cork particle. In this operation more of the hardback is removed, this brittle part of cork being ground much finer than the soft resilient cork. This fine fraction is heavy and settles to the bottom. It is removed by passing the cork over a screen. The cork is next passed on to another mill for further grinding and cleaning.

The cork is now dried in rotary driers to the desired low moisture content and then separated into different sizes by screening. The large particles are returned to the mills for additional grinding while the fine dust which passes through all the screens is removed to a dust silo. The portion of the cork that passes through the coarse screens but is retained on the finer screens is ready for manufacturing into composition cork and is stored until needed.

One thousand pounds of good quality corkwood will yield from 600 to 700 pounds of clean granulated cork. This loss is not great when the relative weights of pure, light cork and hardback are considered. Hardback is about five to eight times as heavy as clean cork. The consecutive grinding, air-floating, and screening operations remove all hard and foreign matter from cork and the granulated product is soft and uniformly pure. This thorough processing is carried out so that the composition cork manufactured will be of uniform quality.

From storage bins the granulated cork is air conveyed to the mixing rooms. Here, in suitable mixing equipment, the cork particles are coated with a free-flowing adhesive binder which can readily be converted into a tough, elastic material by the application of heat. Several types of adhesives are used for making composition cork, the particular type selected depending on the application of the finished composition. Liners for food container caps must contain a binder free from taste or odor which gives a tough, strong and resilient composition. Gasket composition cork for machinery must have an oil-resistant binder which is so blended with the cork that the resultant composition exhibits no substantial shrinkage or expansion when cut into long narrow gaskets.

The granulated cork is accurately measured on automatic scales, emptied into the mixer and the calculated amount of binder added. Finely granulated cork requires more adhesive binder per pound because it has a greater surface area to be covered. For example, a 1-inch cube has a total surface area of 6 sq. in. Now, if we divide this cube into small cubes, each having a side one-tenth of an inch, we obtain 1000 cubes. Each of these small cubes has a surface area of six-hundredths of 1 sq. in., and the total surface of them all is 60 sq. in. By subdivision we have increased the surface area ten times.

After thorough mixing in which each granule of cork is coated with a thin film of binder, the coated cork may pass to a bin for temporary storage or be used immediately. The binder-coated cork is carefully measured and packed into tubes for rod production or pressed into large molds for block manufacture. The tubes or molds are heated slowly to permit penetration of the packed cork. The actual temperature of baking varies with the nature of the composition and depends upon the character of the adhesive binder used and the ultimate application of the composition.

(*Courtesy, Crown Cork & Seal Co.*)

Gaskets of composition cork, made in many sizes and designs, are used for sealing parts of machinery when the unit is assembled.

After baking, the tubes are cooled and the rods are ejected. The rods are stacked in racks where they are allowed to season. When ready for use the rods are fed into slicing machines which rapidly cut discs of the correct thickness. The discs pass over assorting tables where, under the watchful eyes of trained sorters, any imperfect ones are removed.

Composition cork liners are assembled in crown caps by high-speed automatic machines. The metal caps and composition cork liners are conveyed to separate compartments near the assembly machines. From these compartments they are brought together by the machines, from which they emerge as units. A final inspection is given the caps and liners as they pass from the assembly machines.

Composition cork is manufactured in block form in several convenient sizes and shapes. There are no particular limits to the size of these blocks but such factors as handling the heavy molds, duration of the heating period and processing the large blocks usually control the dimensions. However, blocks as large as 5 ft by 2 ft. by 3 in. can readily be manufactured.

The process for making composition cork blocks is much the same as for the manufacture of rods. Granulated cork is coated with suitable adhesives and conveyed to the packing rooms. Of course, the coated cork may be stored if this is desirable. The coated cork is weighed on automatic scales and emptied in the molds. To ensure uniformity in the finished block the coated granulated cork is distributed evenly throughout the mold. The cork is then compressed and the mold is closed. Pressing the cork forces out air which is between the granules and permits the binder-coated particles to be in close contact. The molds pass into a heating chamber or oven where sufficient heat to insolubilize the binder is maintained. The duration of the curing period depends upon many factors, such as the nature of the adhesive employed, the thickness of the molds and the density of the composition cork being manufactured. As the molds pass from the heating chamber they are cooled and the blocks of composition cork removed. Generally, the composition cork blocks are stored for seasoning, being so arranged as to permit the circulation of air about and through the stacks. When ready for use they are cut into sheets of the desired thickness. Slicing may be effected by passing the block against a rapidly revolving large circular knife or by employing a machine similar to that used in the plywood industry. Closure liners, gaskets of various sizes and shapes, shoe insoles, table mats and numerous other articles are cut from composition cork sheets.

Continuous sheet composition cork is manufactured by packing granulated cork which has been coated with a suitable adhesive into a large cylindrical mold. After the block has been made and seasoned it is sliced into a long continuous sheet. The slicing is effected by causing the block to revolve against a sharp knife and the sheet formed is simultaneously wound into a compact roll. The length of the continuous sheet depends upon the thickness to which it is sliced. Sheets of any desired thickness, from one-thirty-second up to three-sixteenths of an inch may be cut. After the sheeting operation, the wide roll may be divided into a number of narrow rolls. This form of cork is often called ribbon cork and has many applications in the closure field as well as other industrial uses.

By varying the density of the cork blocks, composition for almost any desired purpose can be prepared. Changes in the density are effected by altering the type and quantity of the adhesive binder employed, by varying the particle size of the granulated cork and by employing different amounts of the binder-coated cork. Through such changes in formulation and manufacture, cork composition can be produced to meet a wide range of industrial requirements. A soft resilient composition must be used for sealing glass, while dense and hard compositions are required for other applications. Thus, the reader can readily see that composition cork is available in properties and dimensions for many industrial applications that natural cork cannot serve.

Sheets of composition cork are used in the manufacture of liners for many types of closures which require sizes not conveniently made in the rod form. Such liners are produced by slicing the composition cork block to the correct thickness and causing the sheet to pass under rapidly revolving cutting dies. Sometimes several layers of the sheet cork are cut at once. Liners for many sizes of caps are manufactured in this way—from the small caps used on toothpaste tubes to those for large screw caps.

After sealing liners for crown caps and other types of closures, the next important use of composition cork is in the manufacture of industrial gaskets. Hundreds of cork gaskets are used in motors, in many parts of automobiles, in meters of every description, and in many types of machinery. Cork gaskets are employed to keep in oil and to keep out moisture, air and dust. Being light, compressible, resilient, waterproof, resistant to penetration by oils and solvents, and chemically stable, composition cork gaskets give effective and permanent sealing.

Composition cork is also much used in the manufacture of bathing shoes, beach sandals, house slippers, and shoe inner soles. The high coefficient of friction of composition cork gives to the user of cork-soled footwear a firmness and sureness of step not obtained with other water-resistant soles. By combining cork with colored adhesives many attractive compositions can be made which may be used with beach costumes to give matching or contrasting colors. Composition cork insoles give a softness and warmth not obtained by any other material without substantially increasing the bulk or weight or both.

Composition cork stereotype blankets may be employed in the printing of our daily newspapers. The cork blanket or pad is used in the process of transferring the linotype negative to an embossed positive on a specially prepared paper board. The paper board positive is later used in making a negative on cast metal. Compressibility and rapid recovery are essential in this work and the unique physical properties of cork make it a most satisfactory material for this purpose.

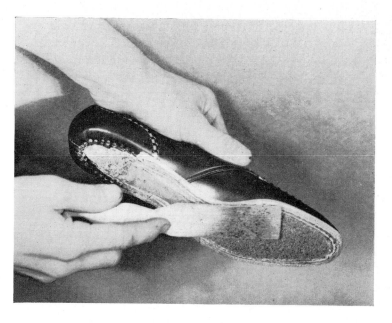

(*Courtesy, Cork Institute of America*)

Special composition cork used as a filler in the bottom of shoes adds resiliency.

Composition cork novelties such as scrapbook covers, waste baskets, lamp shades, desk pads and letter holders make attractive and pleasing articles. An inexpensive metal waste basket when covered with composition cork becomes noiseless and more attractive. Photograph albums are made up with a fine particle composition cork cover on to which letters from large granule composition cork are bonded.

There are numerous other uses of composition cork. Every day in some manner, directly or indirectly, cork and composition cork affect the life of the average individual.

CHAPTER VII

CORKBOARD

Heat and cold are nature's two hands by which she
chiefly worketh.

FRANCIS BACON

A LARGE percentage of the world's annual production of corkwood is
consumed in the manufacture of cork insulation board. The extensive
use today of domestic refrigerators and deep freeze cabinets, the rapid
expansion of modern air conditioning and the widespread need of cold
storage warehouses and freezer lockers create a tremendous demand for
low temperature insulation materials. Natural cork, because of its air-
filled cellular structure, possesses a high resistance to the passage of heat.
One of the most efficient systems for thermal insulation is still air in finely
divided spaces. In cork we have just such a material and for centuries
natural corkbark has been used by residents in the cork-producing
countries to help keep their houses warm in the winter and cool during
the summer. The tiny air-filled cells—there are more than two hundred
million cells in 1 cubic inch of cork—provide an effective barrier to the
flow of heat. The present-day methods of manufacturing corkboard
insulation increase the natural resistance to heat transfer which is inherent
in cork. Compared with competitive low temperature insulation materials
corkboard stands high in insulating efficiency.

The use of cork for insulation purposes had its beginning centuries ago
in the cork-producing countries. Corkbark laid on the tops of houses
provided homes with protection from the extreme heat of the summer's
sun. During the winter months cork placed on the floors and walls
maintained warm homes with even temperatures. Early monasteries made
similar use of cork. Later on, cork was incorporated in the walls of
buildings by mixing pieces of broken corkwood with earth and from this
mixture forming the walls. However, the use of cork as a low temperature
insulation material during ancient and medieval times was very limited

and only in the past 60 years has corkboard insulation become a major industrial commodity.

About 1890 a German company acquired patent rights in Germany and the United States for a new type of cork insulation known as "Impregnated Corkboard". This product was well received and "impregnated" cork slabs were generally used for insulating cold storage rooms. Impregnated cork was in reality a composition cork in which large granules of

(*Courtesy, Crown Cork & Seal Co.*)
Corkboard insulation is accurately trimmed
to the desired size and then packaged.

cork were bonded together with a special type of clay. This form of corkboard had its weak points but at that time it served an important field of industry and demands for the product grew. However, in a few years this product was found to be much inferior to a new type of cork insulation which was pure corkboard. The manufacture of pure corkboard for insulation began in the eighteen-nineties and the story of its invention reads like fiction.

The discovery of the process of baking cork particles under pressure to bind them together in a single mass was an accident. The unique way in which this happened is effectively told by Thomas.[71] We read:

In the "Boat Works" of John T. Smith on lower South Street, on the East River, in New York, was a large cast-iron kettle with a fire box under it, the kettle being used to steam oak framing for row boats that Smith manufactured there for many years. He also produced boat fenders, life preservers and ring buoys, in the manner common in those days, by packing granulated cork in canvas jackets. Girls packed the cork in these jackets, using tin forms or cylinders to keep the canvas distended until filled. One of these cylinders became clogged in the hands of one of Smith's employees and was laid aside for the moment, but it inadvertently rolled into the dying embers of the fire box during clean-up late that evening.

Early the next morning, Smith, owner and fireman, cleaned out the fire box and found his misplaced utensil. But the hot ashes had not consumed the cork particles that had clogged it. The heat had been sufficient merely to bind the mass together in the form of a very substantial chocolate-brown cork cylinder.

Smith noted this peculiar fact with much interest, if not with actual astonishment, and put the tin form and cork cylinder aside for future secret study and investigation. He repeated the original and wholly unintentional experiment enough times to satisfy himself that for some good reason a certain degree of heat applied for a given time served to glue cork particles together without the addition of a foreign substance or binder of any kind or character, to produce what he later termed "Smith's Consolidated Cork". He thereupon applied for and was granted basic patents in the United States, Germany, France and England covering the broad principles involved.

Since the invention by John Smith many improvements have been made in the manufacture of corkboard insulation. Several processes are employed today, and each is based on the discovery made by Smith over 60 years ago that cork expands when heated and some of the resins are brought to the surface.

In the manufacture of corkboard insulation, cork is granulated into coarse particles, which are transferred to molds that are covered securely. In one process superheated steam at approximately 550° to 600°F is passed through the cork. Another method is by oven-baking, which is slower and requires 4–6 hours at temperatures ranging from 500° to 600°F. Blocks of corkboard vary in dimensions and they are cut into slabs and trimmed. A usual size is 12 in. by 36 in. by 1 in., but pieces 1.5 and 2 in. thick are also standard sizes. Larger slabs can be obtained if desired. The baking operation removes from cork some of the more volatile constituents which, together with expansion, yields a product of low density. Trimmed corkboard insulation weighs from 6.5 to 9 pounds per cubic foot.

Installation of corkboard insulation is carried out by trained workmen. Each section of corkboard is covered with a continuous film of asphalt. Then the coated corkboard is put in place while the asphalt film is hot. In this way the asphalt coating serves also as an adhesive. The sections of low density corkboard are held together in a single piece and also are bonded to the walls against which the insulation is installed. Corkboard is highly resistant to moisture and the asphalt coating applied during installation increases this natural resistance to water vapor. Corkboard insulation is durable and its insulating efficiency is retained years after installation.

Cork insulation is manufactured for pipe covering and used on pipes carrying cold water, brine and other cold materials. Cork pipe insulation increases the efficiency of the cold pipe system. Also, sweating or moisture condensation on the cold pipes under conditions of high humidity is prevented. Cork insulation for pipes is molded to the correct size to fit both the pipes and the connections. When cork pipe covering is installed a coating of asphalt is applied inside and outside.

Sometimes granulated corkboard is employed for insulation. This form of cork can be blown into the walls and other areas of buildings where corkboard slabs cannot be placed without extensive work. The corkboard granules provide efficient insulation for years as the light particles do not settle and cause the insulating filling to become denser.

Corkboard is employed also for machinery isolation and acoustical purposes. For machinery isolation heavier corkboard is required than for thermal insulation. The density varies up to 24 pounds per cubic foot, and loads as high as 8000 pounds per square foot are carried. The corkboard absorbs jolts, reduces vibration and noise, and thus prolongs the life of the mounted machine.

Low density corkboard, weighing about 5.5 pounds per cubic foot, is used for correcting indoor sound reflections which are called reverberations. The porous surface that is characteristic of corkboard is excellent for absorbing sound waves and reducing noise. For decorative purposes the dark acoustical material often is given a white or light colored coating of suitable paint, on the surface which will be exposed after installation. Acoustical corkboard, also, is an efficient thermal insulator and therefore performs a double service wherever installed.

CHAPTER VIII

MISCELLANEOUS CORK PRODUCTS

Nature is ever making signs to us, she is ever whisper-
ing to us the beginnings of her secrets; the scientific
man must be ever on the watch, ready at once to lay
hold of nature's hint, however small.

SIR MICHAEL FOSTER

CORK tile is a luxurious type of flooring that provides real comfort, can be obtained in different shades and may be used for many years. Cork tile consists only of cork and contains no adhesive binders or other added materials. It is prepared principally from cork shavings that are obtained when natural cork stoppers are tapered.

The development of the cork tile industry progressed slowly at first. Beginning about 1900 the industry made little growth for 20 years. However, in the limited places where cork tile had been installed, quiet, resilient and durable floors gave comfort and satisfaction that became widely known.

Cork tile production expanded sharply from 1920 to 1927. During the depression years the quantity of cork tile manufactured dropped to a comparatively low figure. In the past 10 years the demand for cork tile has increased again and today more than 3,000,000 square feet of cork tile are manufactured annually.

Cork in the form of tile makes an attractive, resilient floor that is quiet and warm. Cork tile is especially suitable as a floor material for churches, concert halls, hospitals and libraries, but it is used also in some of the finer homes and shops.

The older form of cork tile is manufactured by baking cork shavings and particles while highly compressed. Heat applied for baking causes the air-filled cork cells to expand and fill every void between the particles. Since the cork is confined in a strong mold under high pressure the tendency to expand under heat causes the cork particles to interlock into a single mass. At the same time some of the resins in cork are brought to the surface of the cork particles by the heat. These resins aid in holding the cork particles together as a unit.

In this process the shavings and granules are packed and compressed in strong molds by hydraulic pressure. The molds are transferred into ovens where the cork is baked from 7 to 10 hours at 450° to 600°F. Cork baked for 10 hours at 600° is darker in color than cork baked for a shorter time at a lower temperature. By varying the length of the baking period

(*Courtesy, Colonial Williamsburg, Inc.*)

Cork tile walls add restfulness to this waiting room at the Information Center, Williamsburg, Virginia.

and the temperature different shades of cork tile can be produced. Cork tile is manufactured in three shades designated as light brown, medium brown and dark brown. These shades are employed in floors to give contrasting color effects and to produce attractive patterns.

After removal from the molds, cork tile is sawed into squares or rectangles of a variety of sizes. The pieces may be as small as 3 in. by 3 in. or as large as 18 in. by 36 in. Cork tile may be obtained in several thicknesess, from $\frac{1}{4}$ in. to $\frac{1}{2}$ in.

While originally a floor material, in recent years cork tile has been used also as a wall covering. Cork tile is installed by merely cementing it to the floor or wall which should be smooth and level.

A cork tile floor is very durable. Even after years of service, when resanded and refinished a cork tile floor has the appearance of a new installation. Because of its long life combined with comfort and satisfaction cork tile floors are competitive with other high quality floor materials.

In recent years a product of cork and vinyl resin has been manufactured as both a floor and wall covering. This vinyl cork material possesses all of the well-known desirable qualities of cork, namely, quietness, resiliency, warmth and durability, plus the high resistance of vinyl to wear and cleaning. The vinyl surface coating, being transparent, permits the attractive pattern of the cork to be seen.

Linoleum, a well-known and widely used type of floor covering, contains a limited quantity of cork. It is manufactured as rugs, in roll form for wall to wall application, and in tile form. Also, like cork tile, linoleum is manufactured in thicknesses to make it suitable as a wall covering.

Linoleum was first produced in England, having been developed in 1863 by Frederick Walton of Yorkshire. It was an outgrowth of earlier, cruder types of floor coverings.

Originally, linoleum contained four essential materials, namely, oxidized linseed oil, resins, cork and burlap base or backing. In the early forms of linoleum cork particles as large as one-eighth of an inch across were used but tests and time showed fine cork gave the same resiliency and greater durability. Today, high quality linoleum consists of these same basic materials, or alternate substances, and in addition other materials such as gums, woodfloor, inorganic fillers and pigments.

The quantity of cork in linoleum is small and it is thoroughly mixed with the other materials. Cork has been retained in linoleum because it contributes resiliency to the finished product.

Cork is employed in several ways to help produce better and more comfortable footwear. Cork inner soles in shoes provide warmth, resiliency and lightness. The cork inner soles may be cut from natural cork but more often they are of composition cork.

In manufacturing the inner soles several sheets of cork are laid one above the other in a press and the cutting dies placed on top. When ready, the top of the press is brought down quickly with force and the razor sharp edges of the dies cut through the layers of cork forming the soles.

Cork is used also in preparing the bottom filler of shoes. Granulated cork is mixed with a resilient thermoplastic adhesive and the cork composition is spread between the welt of the leather sole. This cork filler gives additional softness and comfort to shoes.

Other applications of composition cork in shoes are in the box toe and the counter, which is connected with the heel.

Special abrasive wheels are prepared from granulated cork and used to polish glass and ceramic products. By carefully choosing the type of adhesive binder and employing the proper degree of compression polishing wheels of the desired degree of hardness can be prepared. Of course, the size of the cork particles employed and ratio of binder to cork are important. Composition cork is used to polish plate glass which gives clear vision.

The high coefficient of friction of cork which makes it valuable in polishing wheels is utilized further in textile mills in the form of rolls. These composition cork rolls are known in industry as cots and they are used in the spinning of cotton and other fibers. The cork cots possess the right degree of friction to maintain the fibers at proper tension.

Cork also plays an important role in high temperature insulation. Insulating bricks manufactured from clay, diatomaceous earth and fine waste cork are very efficient. They are used in ovens, superheaters and furnaces.

The process of making this type of fire brick is unusual. Waste cork accumulates when corkboard is trimmed. This waste cork is ground to a fine, uniform size and then is mixed with clay, diatomaceous earth and water. This mixture when homogeneous is pressed into bricks which are loaded on cars for firing. Specially constructed long kilns are employed for firing the bricks.

The first car is loaded with wood which heats the kiln as it burns. The bricks then pass through the kiln and the cork in the bricks begins to burn slowly. The burning cork raises the temperature of the kiln and with certain types of brick it is necessary to cool the kiln. During the firing, which may last two days, every particle of cork is completely burned. At the exit end of the kiln the bricks are slowly cooled and, as the cars pass out, the bricks are sized.

A good high temperature insulating brick should have high porosity with very small pores. Low density is also desirable. As the tiny cork particles which are distributed uniformly throughout the bricks burn small voids are formed. Each brick contains thousands of such voids. Bricks manufactured by this process are light and possess low heat conductivity. While no cork is present in the finished bricks, cork is essential in their manufacture.

A recent invention covers the use of cork in bowling pins. From the center of the base of the pin a hole about 1 inch in diameter is bored for several inches and a cork rod is forced into this opening. The resilient cork absorbs the shock when a ball strikes the pin and prolongs the useful life of the pin.

A well-known use of composition cork is the manufacture of bulletin boards. Thumb tacks are easily pushed into the soft cork and when removed the resiliency of cork causes the voids made by the tacks to close. For this reason bulletin boards of composition cork usually outlast those of competitive materials.

Novelties of cork are widely used. These may be of composition cork or natural cork. In the cork-producing countries intricately carved boxes, pictures and other items of natural cork are available in gift shops. Both composition cork and natural cork are employed in manufacturing lamp shades, desk pads and calendars. Limbs and branches of cork trees having the attractive gray virgin corkbark and olive green foliage are used in decorating shop windows.

CHAPTER IX

PRODUCTION AND TRADE DATA

To business that we love we rise betime, And go to
it with delight.

WILLIAM SHAKESPEARE

THE increasing demands for cork products in the United States and other countries during the past 60 years have had a beneficial effect on the economy of the cork-producing countries of the world. The expanding uses and growing commercial importance of cork and cork products have directed the attention of both private and governmental owners to the value of the cork trees. Realizing that cork was an essential commodity and the need for it steadily increasing, steps were taken to conserve the cork forests and to extend the areas devoted to cork trees by additional plantings. As a result better care has been given to the cork forests in all of the cork-producing countries. Private owners have shown interest in preserving their holdings and the national governments have established regulations covering the proper care of the cork trees. Reforestation and culture of cork oaks have been subjects of study and experimentation. This attention to cork trees has resulted in a marked increase in cork production in the past 40 years in all of the cork-producing countries.

Much of the cork produced is shipped in the raw or unmanufactured state. For this reason proper marketing conditions and methods have been established. Before baling, the cork is correctly graded and bales of the various grades are carefully marked. Quality standards describe the different grades. Today, cork buyers purchase their requirements with confidence knowing cork is of the quality indicated by the outer pieces of the bales.

Portugal is the world's largest producer of cork and supplies approximately 50 percent of the total cork harvested annually. The average annual yield of corkwood is 170,000 metric tons, although in some years this figure is exceeded. About 80 percent of Portugal's cork is exported

(*Courtesy, Portuguese Embassy*)
Cork in Portugal, stacked and ready to be sold.

in the unmanufactured state. Approximately 33 percent of the world's cork-producing area is located in Portugal. The total area of the country's cork forests amounts to about 1,720,000 acres. These facts place Portugal in a very important position in the cork industry and make cork one of the country's principal products.

Within the last 35 years annual production of cork in Portugal has increased threefold.

During the same period Portuguese exports of unmanufactured cork have remained high while exports of cork products show a sharp rise.

Spain stands second in importance in corkwood production and plays a leading part in the world-wide cork industry. During the thirties cork production declined in Spain but in recent years has become readjusted.

TABLE I*

CORK PRODUCTION, PORTUGAL

Year	Metric Tons	Year	Metric Tons
1925	56,534	1950	173,779
1930	84,283	1955	189,657
1935	95,040	1956	191,443
1940	59,673	1957	166,405
1945	150,026	1958	142,993

TABLE II*

EXPORTS OF RAW CORK (CORKWOOD, WASTE, SHAVINGS, ETC.), PORTUGAL

Year	Metric Tons	Value (1000 Escudos)
1935	128,579	99,655
1940	134,316	156,614
1945	116,478	241,418
1950	168,268	453,704
1955	122,178	949,643
1956	104,985	822,361
1957	93,051	648,416
1958	107,305	612,033

TABLE III*

EXPORTS OF MANUFACTURED AND SEMI-MANUFACTURED CORK PRODUCTS, PORTUGAL

Year	Metric Tons	Value (1000 Escudos)
1925	11,986	14,642
1930	18,423	44,022
1935	17,429	49,786
1940	18,221	135,404
1945	25,530	261,421
1950	39,722	431,922
1955	37,770	751,559
1956	37,997	744,151
1957	40,127	718,879
1958	39,155	691,865

* Data in Tables I, II and III from statistics supplied through courtesy of the Portuguese Embassy, Washington, D.C.

The extent of the cork forests in Spain is difficult to accurately state. The cork oak is frequently found with other species, *Quercus ilex* in particular. About 84 percent of the cork forest area also serves as grazing grounds. Various reports give the area of Spanish cork forests from 830,000 to 1,100,000 acres. However, a more realistic estimate of the cork forests of Spain is given at 800,000 acres.

Under normal conditions Spain can produce from 75,000 to 100,000 metric tons of cork annually. Of the total production normal domestic consumption yearly amounts to from 15,000 to 20,000 metric tons and the balance is utilized in export trade.

TABLE IV*

CORK PRODUCTION, SPAIN

Year	Tons	Value (1000 Pesetas)
1940	61,000	—
1946	62,533	16,081
1947	55,196	15,135
1948	70,531	21,832
1949	35,416	10,315
1950	67,835	39,182
1951	90,556	171,060
1952	62,030	93,211
1953	48,966	97,886
1954	72,007	262,826
1955	98,416	370,077
1956	58,705	154,570
1957	77,447	261,982

* Data from statistics supplied through courtesy of the Spanish Embassy, Washington, D.C.

The cork area of Spanish Morocco has been given widely varying estimates. Government-owned cork forests in 1942 amounted to 67,000 acres. The total cork forests of Spanish Morocco amounts to 75,000 to 80,000 acres. The potential annual yield is estimated at 6000 metric tons. Spanish Morocco has no cork factories and the entire yearly production is exported in the unmanufactured state.

TABLE V*

EXPORTS OF RAW CORK (CORKWOOD, WASTE, SHAVING, ETC.),
SPAIN

Year	Metric Tons	Value (1000 Pesetas)
1930	32,928	16,178
1935	25,749	4,217
1940	34,743	7,227
1946	21,415	7,491
1950	43,297	49,696
1956	30,448	63,222
1957	30,135	52,433
1958	34,911	55,848

TABLE VI*

EXPORTS OF MANUFACTURED CORK PRODUCTS, SPAIN

Year	Metric Tons	Value (1000 Pesetas)
1930	30,491	89,624
1935	15,465	18,523
1940	11,093	9,372
1946	19,051	23,070
1956	19,937	121,590
1957	17,451	104,105
1958	18,705	102,575

* Data in from statistics supplied through courtesy of
the Spanish Embassy, Washington, D.C.

Cork oak forests in France covered a larger area in the past than they
do today. Because of reforestation with different trees and other factors
the cork oak area has been reduced considerably. Today, the cork
forests in France, including the island of Corsica, cover an area of approximately 350,000 acres. While over one-half of the French cork forests are
privately owned a large portion of the cork-producing area is controlled
by the French Government. Annual production under normal conditions
is placed at 12,000 metric tons, which is not sufficient for domestic demands.
Considerable cork, both raw and manufactured, is imported from Spain

TABLE VII*

CORK EXPORTS, FRANCE

Year	Metric Tons	Value (1000 Francs)
1950	2370	138,936
1955	7132	534,870
1956	5708	435,907
1957	3427	291,372
1958	4176	443,661

and North Africa. The manufacture of cork products is a well-developed industry in France.

Algeria is the largest of the North African countries producing cork. The cork forest area is quite extensive, the total amounting to approximately 1,100,000 acres. The French Government controls and operates about 55 percent of the total cork area and the balance is handled by townships, companies and private individuals. The cork trees in Algeria differ widely in size, age, the number of trees per acre and the quality of corkbark. This results in variations in the quantity of cork produced per acre as well as the variations in the price. The average annual production from both private and government forests amounts to 40,000 metric tons. Most of the Algerian cork is exported in the unmanufactured state. However, a small percentage of the annual yield is consumed domestically in the manufacture of corkboard insulation, stoppers and other cork products.

TABLE VIII*

CORK PRODUCTION, ALGERIA

Year	Metric Tons	Year	Metric Tons
1930	10,223	1955	41,100
1935	10,420	1956	5,900
1940	29,086	1957	3,700
1945	24,545	1958	3,600
1950	32,764		

* Data in Tables VII and VIII from statistics supplied through courtesy of the Embassy of France, Washington, D.C.

Exports of raw cork from Algeria in 1954 were 66,978 metric tons. This is a quantity higher than the cork produced for that year and shows that accumulated cork was appreciably reduced.

French Morocco contains a large cork forest area which amounts to about 760,000 acres. Included in this area is the famous Mamora forest which covers more than 300,000 acres. Here the trunks of the cork trees are comparatively straight. In other locations stands of cork oaks are mixed with other trees. Cork production is estimated at 18,000 metric tons annually. The domestic consumption of cork in French Morocco is low and most of the annual production is exported in either manufactured or unmanufactured condition. Until recent years practically all of this

TABLE IX*

CORK PRODUCTION, FRENCH MOROCCO

Year	Metric Tons	Year	Metric Tons
1923	255	1946	20,117
1928	6,209	1950	14,950
1933	6,709	1955	23,994
1938	20,240	1956	17,800

EXPORTS OF RAW AND MANUFACTURED CORK, FRENCH MOROCCO

Year	Metric Tons	Value (1000 Francs)
1925	5,736	1,489
1930	9,220	4,973
1935	10,846	3,162
1940	7,692	13,549
1945	5,967	28,859
1950	29,412	83,084
		Value (Million Francs)
1955	35,658	2,347
1956	34,341	2,050
1957	40,817	2,234
1958	31,847	2,639

* Data from statistics supplied through courtesy of the Embassy of Morocco, Washington, D.C.

cork was exported in the unmanufactured state. Today cork stoppers and corkboard for insulation are manufactured in French Morocco.

Although the cork tree is not new to Tunisia, commercial cork production is less than 70 years old. The Tunisian forestry administration was established in 1884 and the first stripping of virgin cork was carried out in 1892. Prior to that time the cork trees were exploited by anybody who wanted the cork. The cork forests in Tunisia cover about 280,000 acres. Annual production amounts to about 7000 metric tons. Practically the entire yield is exported in the unmanufactured state. However, cork manufacturing has been initiated and exports of manufactured cork from Tunisia will be on the increase.

TABLE X*

CORK PRODUCTION, TUNISIA

Year	Metric Tons	Year	Metric Tons
1925	4730	1945	2281
1930	4703	1950	4435
1935	4710	1955	6948
1940	6941	1956	

CORK EXPORTS, TUNISIA

Year	Metric Tons	Year	Metric Tons
1925	6705	1945	833
1930	3660	1950	4355
1935	3765	1955	10,299
1940	5463	1956	

* Data from statistics supplied through courtesy of the Embassy of Tunisia, Washington, D.C.

The total area of the cork forests of Italy is estimated at about 200,000 acres. Of this area approximately 65 percent is in Sardinia and 20 percent is in Sicily. As in other countries the cork forests in Italy today are considerably reduced from their former size. The amount of cork harvested varies from year to year because of market fluctuations. The annual production averages 11,000 metric tons but in 1941 the total cork

F

harvest exceeded 16,000 metric tons.   Unlike France, more cork is
exported from Italy than is brought into the country. From 1930 to 1942
annual cork exports from Italy averaged 4878 metric tons which was
approximately two and a half times the average yearly imports for the
same period.

In the United States during the past 35 years imports of unmanufactured

TABLE XI*

CORK IMPORTS, ITALY

Unmanufactured Cork

Year	Metric Tons	Value (1000 Lire)
1950	572	37,962
1955	1514	365,697
1956	1926	483,502
1957	3469	713,352
1958	7010	1,412,111

Manufactured Cork

Year	Metric Tons	Value (1000 Lire)
1950	100	5654
1955	752	290,018
1956	796	322,970
1957	2151	714,535
1958	1892	693,197

TABLE XII*

CORK EXPORTS, ITALY

Unmanufactured Cork

Year	Metric Tons	Value (1000 Lire)
1950	6118	388,256
1955	8943	1,927,175
1956	6968	1,406,129
1957	1495	455,588
1958	1619	567,850

Manufactured Cork

Year	Metric Tons	Value (1000 Lire)
1950	587	171,921
1955	1256	483,050
1956	2700	994,066
1957	2428	927,903
1958	2485	861,802

* Data in Tables XI and XII from statistics supplied through courtesy of the Italian Embassy, Washington, D.C.

TABLE XIII†

IMPORTS, UNMANUFACTURED CORK, UNITED STATES

Year	Pounds	Value (dollars)
1925	213,659,000	2,995,000
1930	174,614,000	5,498,000
1935	153,075,000	3,057,000
1940	210,932,600	6,320,000
1945	265,453,206	9,008,914
1950	278,201,902	10,660,937
1955	255,361,875	17,750,904
1956	168,967,275	12,094,947
1957	141,309,123	9,057,269
1958	114,917,321	6,769,107

† Data from statistics supplied through courtesy of the Bureau of Census, U.S. Department of Commerce, Washington, D.C.

cork have shown some increase and have remained high during the past 10 years.

The above figures also reflect a sharp rise in the price of cork during this period. This increase in cost has not reduced our imports and the same tonnage of cork is needed today as 10 years ago.

Cork manufactures have kept pace with imports and the dollar value of cork products shows a similar increase during the past third of a century.

The greater part of cork products manufactured in the United States is for domestic consumption. However, the quantity, as well as the value,

TABLE XIV*

CORK MANUFACTURES, UNITED STATES

Year	Value (dollars)	Year	Value (dollars)
1921	12,967,768	1937	21,783,000
1927	17,965,256	1939	17,724,000
1929	23,656,117	1947	35,100,000
1931	12,470,843	1950	25,968,000
1935	13,987,000	1954	39,968,000

of cork products exported during recent years has shown a substantial increase.

TABLE XV*

EXPORTS, MANUFACTURED CORK, UNITED STATES

Year	Pounds	Value (dollars)
1925	—	1,492,000
1930	—	1,043,000
1935	1,446,000	552,000
1940	3,517,000	1,359,000
1945	8,024,692	2,208,258
1950	14,049,261	3,791,698
1955	13,621,467	4,407,400
1956	12,275,255	4,628,483
1957	12,727,933	4,880,843
1958	10,294,726	3,999,773

* Data in Tables XIV and XV from statistics supplied through courtesy of the Bureau of Census, U.S. Department of Commerce, Washington, D.C.

During the past 100 years efforts have been made by other countries to establish the cork oak within their boundaries. Argentina, Australia, Soviet Russia, United States and Uruguay have attempted to grow cork trees. The history and results in the United States are covered in the following pages. Elsewhere the information available regarding the extent of the plantings or the outcome of the experiments is limited. While unfavorable reports on some of the planting tests have been

(Courtesy, Crown Cork & Seal Co.)

A boatload of cork arrives in Baltimore. Because cork is light it is loaded
on the deck and heavier cargo is carried in the ship's hold.

reported other attempts have had encouraging results. A few cork trees
have resulted from these efforts but it is doubtful that sufficient trees for
any commercial production cork will be obtained for quite some time.

CHAPTER X

EARLY CORK OAK PLANTINGS
IN THE UNITED STATES

The trees in the streets are old trees
used to living with people,
Family-trees that remember your
grandfather's name.

STEPHEN VINCENT BENÉT

CORK oak trees in limited numbers have been growing in the United States for over 100 years. These few cork trees have originated from cork acorns brought here and planted by persons who knew the tree and desired to grow it. All mature cork trees in the United States have been grown for their beauty as ornamental shade trees. In 1945, the number of mature cork oaks in this country was estimated to be about 3000, most of which were growing in California. Their origin and history are filled with attention holding stories of intrigue and romance.

The earliest record of cork oaks growing in the United States dates back to 1765. John Bartram, the distinguished botanist of that day, in a botanical tour of Georgia, the Carolinas and Florida, discovered a cork tree growing near Charleston, South Carolina. From his diary[72] we read:

July 9 rose early and set out with John Dayeas. . . . we came to ye house of a Good natured Gentleman one Mr. Blake. . . . Here I saw A tree of ye cork oak ten foot high and 8 inches diameter cloathed with A thin coat of cork.

(The name "Dayeas" is more often referred to as "Deas". The plantation of John Deas was about 20 miles north-west of Charleston. There were two Blake plantations on the east side of the Ashley River, a few miles southwest of the Deas place.)

The first person to make a sustained effort to plant and grow cork oak trees in the United States was Thomas Jefferson, the third President.

Mr. Jefferson was a man of many accomplishments. Statesman, architect, sportsman, musician, inventor, agriculturist—the sage of

Monticello was all of these. In his work as a scientific farmer Jefferson improved agricultural tools and introduced new plants. He invented the molding board for plows and for this achievement was awarded honors by several scientific societies of France. He recommended the planting of "new objects of culture" important to our national welfare "for which nature has fitted our country". Among other valuable plants he urged the planting of cork oak trees as he was "persuaded they will succeed". Although discouraged and disappointed by the "nonchalance" of his fellow citizens he continued his "endeavors" and for 40 years labored unsuccessfully to grow cork trees in the United States.

In 1784 Jefferson was sent to France to assist in negotiating treaties of commerce with European countries. While there and during a short visit to England he saw cork oak trees and noted the soil and climatic conditions under which they grew. Possessing an alert agricultural mind he knew the cork oak could be grown in the southern part of the United States. With the vision that characterized all of Jefferson's work he realized the value of the cork oak to our country and resolved to work toward establishing cork trees in the United States.

While abroad, Jefferson was elected to membership in the Agricultural Society of South Carolina and the notification of his election arrived in Paris during an urgent business trip to England. Upon his return to France he acknowledged this greatly appreciated honor in a letter to William Drayton, Chairman of the Society.[73] A quotation from his autographed letter follows:

Paris, May 6, 1786.

Sir:

Perhaps I may render some service, by forwarding to the society such new objects of culture, as may be likely to succeed in the soil and climate of South Carolina. In an infant country, as ours is, these experiments are important. We are probably far from possessing, as yet, all the articles of culture for which nature has fitted our country. To find out these, will require abundance of unsuccessful experiments. But if, in a multitude of these, we make one useful acquisition, it repays our trouble. . . . I expect, in the same season, from the south of France, some acorns of the Cork oak, which I propose for your society, as I am persuaded they will succeed for you. I observed it to grow in England, without shelter; not well, indeed, but so as to give hopes that it would do well with you.

Thos. Jefferson

Wm. Drayton, Esq.

Paris May 6. 1786.

Your favor of Nov. 23. . . . . I expect in
the same season from the South of France, some acorns of
the Cork oak which I propose for your society, as I am per-
-suaded they will succeed with you.

W^m. Drayton esq.

Th: Jefferson

Paris Feb. 6. 1787.

I had the honour of addressing you . . . .
the present serves to inform you that I send with it, to the
care of your delegates in Congress, some acorns of the Cork oak. I am
told they must not be covered above two inches deep.

W^m. Henry Drayton esq.

Th: Jefferson

Dear Sir   Monticello Apr. 27. 26.
      It is time to think of the introduction of the school of Botany
. . . .
The trees I should propose would be exotics of distinguished
usefulness, and accomodated to our climate. such as the Larch. Cedar
of Libanus, Cork-oak . . . .
. . . . and Cork-oak, I can obtain from France.

Doct^r Emmet
Professor of Nat. Hist at the Univ^y. of Virginia   *Th: Jefferson*

Library of Congress

LETTERS SHOWING JEFFERSON'S INTEREST IN GROWING CORK TREES IN THE U. S.
(Courtesy, Crown Cork & Seal Co.)

Thomas Jefferson was familiar with the cork oak and for 40 years worked to
establish the tree in the United States.

Some cork acorns that matured in the southern part of France in the fall of 1786 were obtained by Jefferson in Paris. These were sent to William Drayton for planting in South Carolina. The following excerpt is taken from an autographed letter of Jefferson to Drayton[73]:

Paris, February 6, 1787.

SIR:

The present serves to inform you that I send with it, to the care of your delegate in Congress, some acorns of the Cork oak. I am told that they must not be covered above 2″ deep. Their being pierced by the worm will not affect their power of vegetating.

THOS. JEFFERSON

WM. HENRY DRAYTON, Esq.

More than 3 months later William Drayton wrote to Jefferson acknowledging receipt of the package of cork acorns. The following quotation is taken from an autographed letter of William Drayton to Thomas Jefferson[73]:

Charleston, May 22, 1787.

SIR:

I had the honor to receive your Excellency's letter of the 6th of February with the box of Cork oak acorns. Your former letter miscarried; but the parcel of special St. John seed reached me, tho very lately and I am afraid it is so much injured by the delay (being extremely mouldy) that it will not vegetate; at least there is no appearance of it yet where I planted it in my garden. I return your Excellency's many thanks in the name of our society for your condescending to be a member and being so attentive to the designs of its institution.

WM. DRAYTON

His Excy. THOS. JEFFERSON

Later on the same year Jefferson wrote to William Drayton about rice, cork and other plants.[73] A portion of his letter reads as follows:

Paris, July 30, 1787.

SIR:

By Colonel Franks, in the month of February last, I sent a parcel of acorns of the Cork oak, which I desired him to ask the favor of the Delegates of South Carolina in Congress to forward to you.

THOS. JEFFERSON

WILLIAM DRAYTON, Esq.

No cork trees were established from these acorns. Very probably the majority of the cork acorns lost their viability before William Drayton received them. In Drayton's correspondence with Jefferson he referred to other seeds being injured by mold and the delay in arrival.

In two letters addressed to Bernard McMahon of Philadelphia, Thomas Jefferson listed the cork oak among other plants he desired.[73] From the first of these letters we read:

Monticello, January 13, 1810.

DEAR SIR:

Your favor of Dec. 24 . . . the Cedar of Lebanon and Cork oak are two trees I have long wished to possess, but even if you have them they could only come by water, and in charge of a careful individual. . . .

THOS. JEFFERSON

BERNARD MCMAHON

Two years later Jefferson wrote to Bernard McMahon and again referred to the cork tree.[73] A portion of his letter follows:

Monticello, February 16, 1812.

DEAR SIR:

In your letter of March last . . . and in my answer of April 8 I mentioned a few articles, as also the mode of conveyance, which could not occur till about this time. An opportunity now presents itself of the most fortunate kind. Mr. Harmer Gilmer, a student of medicine now in Philadelphia, and my neighbor, will be setting out on his return to us very soon after your receive this. He will come in the stage and will, I am sure, take charge of any small box you may be so good as to put under his care. . . . I will still add a little to my former wants so as to put me in possession once for all of everything to which my views extend and which I do not now possess . . . trees. Cedar of Lebanon . . . Cork tree. . . .

THOS. JEFFERSON

Mr. BERNARD MCMAHON

Although discouraged Jefferson continued his efforts toward growing cork oaks. From a letter he wrote while at Monticello to James Ronaldson,[73] type founder and horticulturist of Philadelphia, we read:

Monticello, January 12, 1813.

DEAR SIR:

Your favor of November 2nd arrived a little before I set out on a journey on which I was absent between five and six weeks. I have still therefore to return you my thanks for the seeds accompanying it, which shall be duly taken care of, and a communication made to others of such as shall prove valuable. I have been long endeavoring to procure the Cork tree from Europe, but without success. A plant which I brought with me from Paris died after languishing sometime, and of several parcels of acorns received from a correspondent at Marseilles, not one has ever vegetated. I shall continue my endeavors, although disheartened by the nonchalance of our southern fellow citizens, with whom alone they can thrive. It is now twenty-five years since I sent them two shipments (about 500 plants) of the Olive tree of Aix, the finest Olives in the world. If any of them still exist, it is merely as a curiosity in their gardens, not a single orchard of them has been planted.

THOS. JEFFERSON

Mr. RONALDSON

More than 13 years later and almost 40 years after his first effort to establish the cork oak in this country, Jefferson still worked to obtain plantings of the cork tree. From Monticello, he wrote to Dr. John P. Emmett, Professor of Natural History at the University of Virginia, the following[73]:

Monticello, April 27, 1826.

DEAR SIR:

The trees I should propose would be exotics of distinguished usefulness, and accommodated to our climate; such as the Larch, Cedar of Libanus, Cork oak, the Maronnier, Mahogany, the Catachs or Indian rubber tree of Napul (30°), Teak tree, or Indian oak of Burman (23°), the various woods of Brazil, etc. The seed of the Larch can be obtained from a tree at Monticello. Cones of the Cedar of Libanus are in most of our seed shops, but may be had fresh from the trees in the English gardens. The Maronnier and Cork oak, I can obtain from France.

THOS. JEFFERSON

Doct. EMMETT

The difficulties in establishing the cork oak in the United States in Jefferson's time were tremendous. Travel was slow and means of communication limited and time-consuming. The cork acorns sent to South

Carolina in 1787 were $3\frac{1}{2}$ months in transit. Jefferson's untiring efforts from 1786 to within 6 weeks of his death in 1826 to introduce the cork oak in the United States is typical of his perseverance to achieve things of permanent value to his country.

Although there is no record of any cork trees having been established from the plantings made by Thomas Jefferson, his efforts were not in vain.

(*Courtesy, Crown Cork & Seal Co.*)
This cork tree at Napa, California, is the largest in the
United States. Diameter waist high is 60 inches.

Jefferson's continued efforts and repeated recommendations of the cork tree and the sending of cork acorns to members of Congress, created much interest in this tree and a desire to carry out more extensive plantings.

The United States Government became interested in planting cork trees about 1858. Cork oak acorns were obtained from Spain by the Patent Office (the United States Department of Agriculture was not established until 1862) and distributed in the southeastern states and

California. Many of the acorns and young trees of this planting were lost. However, a few trees survived and in a United States Department of Agriculture report written in 1877 by F. B. Hough[74] we read:

> In 1858 and, it is believed, at an earlier period, quantities of acorns from the cork oak were procured from the south of Spain and distributed from the Patent Office to those sections of the country where it was thought they would thrive. A report made at the close of 1875 from Winnsborough, South Carolina, shows that all the acorns planted in 1859 came up and made healthy plants. Three of these are now 24 feet high and over 27 inches in circumference. Two trees, at least, are flourishing at Orangeburg, South Carolina, and there are probably elsewhere in the South examples of successful planting of this tree. The cork oak requires a warm climate, but the southern states and California appear perfectly well adapted to its wants.

Some of the cork oaks that survived this early planting are today magnificent specimens, having large trunks with wide spreading branches.

In 1880 more cork acorns were obtained and distributed to many places in the southern states, Arizona, and California. While some trees from this planting are still alive, many of them were lost. From time to time a few cork trees have been grown through private effort. Also, local plantings have been made in several states. A substantial planting at Chico, California, in 1904 has resulted in more than 600 cork oaks—the largest stand of cork trees in the United States.[75]

About 44 years ago the United States Forest Service made experimental cork oak plantings in South Carolina and Florida. Acorns were obtained from Portugal and fair percentage sprouted. At Sommerville, South Carolina, the cork seedlings were interspaced with pines, only to be destroyed several years later by a fire. In Florida, when the saplings were about 8 feet high, a severe hurricane destroyed most of them. Those left were badly twisted and deformed. In 1942, only three cork oaks remained from this planting.

In 1929, Woodridge Metcalf, Extension Forester, University of California, published a report entitled Cork Oak—A Forest Tree with Possibilities for California.[75] This report shows numerous cork oaks planted at various times from 1858 to 1910 were vigorous trees and had made good growth.

CHAPTER XI

THE McMANUS CORK PROJECT

He that planteth a tree is a servant of God,
He provideth a kindness for many generations,
And faces that he hath not seen shall bless him.

HENRY VAN DYKE

I. ORIGIN AND SCOPE

While on a business trip to the West Coast in 1939, the late Charles E. McManus, former President and Chairman of the Board of the Crown Cork and Seal Company, observed during a motor trip, some trees along the highway in California that reminded him of cork oaks. He was told, however, that they were only native "scrub oaks". But Mr. McManus was not convinced. Having visited the cork forests of Europe and Africa a number of times he was thoroughly familiar with the cork tree and the similarity between these particular "scrub oaks" and cork trees was too great. Later, when his car came to a stop on the campus of Leland Stanford University, a closer view of one of these trees showed definitely it was a cork oak. He requested permission to remove some of the bark, examination of which convinced him that it was an excellent quality of virgin cork. Other cork trees in the state were located, visited and inspected. The cork on all of these trees was of high quality. The cork trees examined by Mr. McManus were of various ages and sizes. All of them were vigorous and apparently in perfect physical condition. With more than 30 years of successful experience in the manufacturing of cork products, Mr. McManus realized the tremendous value of having cork grown in our own country. Plans were made to remove the bark from some of the trees for thorough testing and to collect acorns for planting. The outcome was the establishment by Mr. McManus of a Cork Project.

This undertaking was designed to add to the natural resources of our country and to provide within the United States a source for at least a part of the nation's cork requirements. Growing cork trees is a program requiring many years. Through the Cork Project, Mr. McManus planned to established the *foundations for a cork growing industry*. This could be achieved by having a substantial number of cork trees grown in every state where the conditions were favorable. With this accomplished, those states in which cork trees gave promise of being a suitable tree crop would

(*Courtesy, Crown Cork & Seal Co.*)

Charles E. McManus, former President and Chairman of Crown Cork & Seal Company, who promoted the planting of cork oak trees in this country.

be in a position to make commercial plantings. The trees established through the Cork Project when mature would produce acorn crops sufficient for planting additional trees each year.

Thorough planning was essential in such a program. The cork oak is native to Europe and Africa and the establishing of a large number of these trees in the warmer half of the United States presented quite a number of problems. Very little was known generally about the cork oak and knowledge of the culture of this tree was extremely meagre. While a small number of cork trees were found in eleven states in this country, there were no records covering the plantings, care and growth of these trees. Although scattered cork trees had been growing in the United States for more than 80 years, the cork bark had never been stripped from any of these domestic trees for scientific purposes. The limited number of cork trees growing here had been planted as ornamentals and they made very attractive shade trees. Interest in the cork tree was limited and entirely aesthetic.

It was evident at the beginning of the Cork Project much research on the culture of the cork oak tree would be necessary. There was the collection and distribution of the acorns which under normal conditions are very perishable. The correct nursery methods for growing cork seedlings as well as the proper technique for lifting, packing and planting had to be determined. It was necessary to ascertain in which states the soil and climate were favorable for growing cork trees. The most suitable planting season in the various states must be known. Assurance must be given that high quality cork could be produced in the United States. These and other problems became immediately evident when the Cork Project was initiated.

II. ORGANIZATION AND OPERATION

To aid in this important and extensive plan for growing cork trees in the United States, foresters throughout all of the states in the favorable area were invited to participate. The program was received with tremendous interest and enthusiasm. The United States Forest Service, State Departments of Forestry, Forestry Schools in the universities and Extension Foresters expressed their desire to cooperate. With such support it is only natural the Cork Project made a successful beginning and rapidly expanded. Later, Vocational Agriculture Teachers in many of the states and Local Agricultural Agents in others, cooperated in distributing large quantities of cork acorns to high school boys and girls. Civic organizations, garden clubs, chambers of commerce, various clubs and other groups aided in many important plantings through their members.

To plant trees, seeds are essential. Cork acorns come only from cork trees and when the Cork Project was launched an extensive search for mature cork trees began at once. Through the columns of magazines and newspapers persons knowing about mature cork trees were requested to report them, giving approximate ages, sizes, names of owners and exact locations. The forestry organizations in each state cooperated in locating and reporting many cork trees. Individuals who knew of one or more

Young cork tree, 10 years old, at the author's home in Towson, Maryland.

cork trees reported them, giving their history as well as other details. The number of known cork trees grew rapidly and it was gratifying to discover sufficient cork trees were growing in California to furnish a substantial quantity of cork acorns each year. A total of about 3000 cork trees were located in that state. Other cork oaks, approximately 100 in number, were found in Arizona and the South. The bulk of the acorns came from California each year, but some acorns were obtained from the southern states.

The annual collection, distribution and planting of cork acorns was the principal work of the Cork Project. This had to be done efficiently and properly if the program was to achieve its purpose. However, no extensive planting had ever been carried on with acorns of any kind from native oaks.

Cork acorns ripen and fall from the trees in November and December. If left on the ground they begin to sprout in a few weeks. It was necessary

G

that the acorns be gathered promptly after dropping, before they began
to sprout.   Also, if allowed to stand in burlap sacks under ordinary
conditions, the acorns either become dry and non-viable or they sprout and
deteriorate. This meant prompt collecting and planting or a satisfactory
method of storing and holding the acorns. Tests showed that clean, fresh
cork acorns can be kept viable for several months in *wet* cold storage at a
temperature range of 34 to 38°.

The work of collecting cork acorns and shipping them to cold storage
plants in distribution centers was promptly initiated.   This involved
obtaining permission from owners of cork trees to take the acorns,
securing individuals and groups to gather them, instructing how the
acorns should be collected, inspecting the bagged acorns and supervising
the shipments. This important and tremendous task was handled most
efficiently.

A large portion of the acorns was shipped to the various state foresters
each year. In some states the greater part of these acorns was planted in the
state forest nurseries to produce seedlings. In other states practically the
entire quantity of acorns was distributed to landowners. A substantial
number of acorns was mailed in small packages to individuals for
immediate planting.

Very large plantings were made every year by high school boys and
girls. Through the leadership of the extension foresters, cork acorns were
shipped to local county agents throughout several states. These acorns
were distributed to members of 4-H Clubs. In other states cork plantings
were made by Future Farmers of America and Future Homemakers of
America. Acorns were sent to vocational agriculture teachers for distribution among these high school organizations. Many cork trees were
planted and established by these young people as well as by other groups
of high school students. The interest, enthusiasm and attention given to
planting cork trees by these high school boys and girls were typical of the
thoroughness they apply to other activities.

Special planting instructions were prepared and given to everyone
receiving acorns or seedlings. These instructions told how the planting
sites should be prepared, gave directions for placing the acorns or seedlings
in the ground, pointed out the necessity for protection against rodents and
gave suggestions regarding the care of the trees. Sketches on the instruc-
tion cards and folders illustrated the main points. In all cases those
receiving acorns and seedlings were told to plant them at once.

During the early days of the project old cork trees served to show where new cork plantings might be made. However, there were entire states or sections of a state in which no cork trees could be found that appeared to have climatic conditions similar to areas in which some old cork trees were growing. In order to include all favorable areas in the Cork Project a special study of the temperature, rainfall and soil conditions of the cork forest regions of Europe and Africa was made. Cork acorns and seedlings were distributed to all sections of the country where the climate appeared to be suitable for the cork oak.

CHAPTER XII

ACHIEVEMENTS OF THE McMANUS CORK PROJECT

I think that I shall never see
A poem lovely as a tree.
Poems are made by fools like me,
But only God can make a tree.

JOYCE KILMER

THE Cork Project was definitely unique in character and noteworthy in attainments. The project in its intensive and extensive nature far surpassed all other efforts on record to establish an exotic tree in a new area. Also, it stands out in the efficient, widespread cooperation given by federal, state and local foresters, men trained in tree culture, and laymen, those interested in plants and trees but lacking formal training in this field. Certainly, a large percentage of the accomplishments was due to the helpful support of those who cooperated with the project. With such help and cooperation all favorable sections from the Pacific to the Atlantic Oceans were provided with cork acorns or seedlings or both. At the same time available knowledge about cork culture was assembled and distributed while studies were initiated to determine other factors important for growing cork trees in this country. The number of cork plantings made and the information obtained concerning the cork tree in this country were very substantial.

ACORN COLLECTION AND DISTRIBUTION

When the Cork Project was set up plans were formed promptly to collect acorns from domestic cork trees for new plantings. The acorns ripen in November and December and the first collection was carried out in the fall and winter of 1940–41. These acorns and those obtained in the following year were distributed only in California and Arizona.

With the extension of cork planting into the South many more pounds of acorns were needed. This is shown in the sharp increase in the quantity of acorns collected and distributed during the 1942–43 season. Every cork acorn produced in this country each year was needed. The quantity collected in 1944–45 approached a total of 6 tons, more than 1,000,000 acorns. The total collection for 1946–47 exceeded 7 tons. Even this huge quantity was not sufficient for the demand. Requests were received from every favorable cork-growing area in the country as well as from many sections wholly unsuited for growing cork trees.

The season for collecting cork acorns extends over a 3-month period beginning in November and continuing on into January. Both individuals and groups gathered the acorns, making possible the prompt storing of the much needed seed while fresh. Large collections were made every year at Chico, Fresno and San Francisco. Smaller quantities of acorns were obtained from the more scattered trees in other sections of California. The cork acorns from Davis were unusually large. In general, the larger, older trees produced the better acorns.

The correct, efficient handling of cork acorns was given intensive study at the beginning of the project. Acorns were kept in ordinary cold storage and were found to become dry and non-viable. They were next kept in moist cold storage and under these conditions about 30 percent of the acorns remained viable over a period of 2 to 3 months. It was then decided to keep the acorns *wet* and at temperatures from 34° to 38°F. Under these conditions the acorns showed no appreciable change from December to April. From the appearance of the acorns they could have been kept for 8 months and possibly a year.

Cork acorn distributions by years are shown in the following table:

TABLE I

SEASON	POUNDS OF ACORNS
1940–41	500
1941–42	1,450
1942–43	7,500
1943–44	7,900
1944–45	13,800
1945–46	10,200
1946–47	14,100
1947–48	7,300
1948–49	7,635
GRAND TOTAL	70,385

Cork acorns average about eighty to the pound and the above figures show approximately 5,000,000 cork acorns were distributed during the 9-year period. The bulk of these acorns were planted in twenty states within the potential cork area of the United States. A small portion was distributed to persons in some six other states outside of the theoretical cork area.

The third grade of Lida Lee Tall School, State Teachers College, Towson, Maryland, observe Arbor Day by planting a cork tree. In center, with shovel, is the author's daughter, Dorsey Cooke.

SEEDLING DISTRIBUTION

Special instructions, illustrated with drawings, were prepared for the planting of cork seedlings. These were sent to the cooperating foresters. Also, each individual to whom cork seedlings were shipped received a copy. The planting instructions cautioned nurserymen to keep the roots of the little trees wet at all times and to pack and ship them wet. Planters were instructed how to prepare the planting sites and cautioned to keep the roots of the plants wet until they were safely in the ground. In California and Arizona practically all of the cork plantings were made with seedlings, while in the South both seedlings and acorns were distributed.

Numerous special plantings of cork trees were made each year in various sections of the country. These were in prominent places and served several purposes. Some were carried out at the request of civic groups. All helped to bring the cork tree to the attention of the public with the result more interest and care were given to individual plantings.

STRIPPING CORK TREES

At the beginning of the Cork Project it was imperative to remove the cork from some of the trees growing in the United States and to examine and test thoroughly the quality of the cork. Accordingly, plans were made to strip a number of cork trees in California in 1940. July and August were the months selected, although in subsequent years some stripping was carried out in the month of September. During the summer of 1940 more than 5 tons of cork were removed from trees at Chico, Davis and Napa. This cork was sent to the Research Laboratories of the Crown Cork & Seal Company in Baltimore for complete testing.

The California virgin cork was thoroughly dried and then ground. It was very encouraging to find the yield of good, usable cork to be as high as 60 percent. The figures below give the results of grinding in detail:

GRINDING TEST

Out of 1739 pounds of California Cork:

173 pounds, 8 × 10 cork,	9.95 percent
411 pounds, 10 × 18 cork,	23.63 percent
102 pounds, 18 × 30 cork,	5.86 percent
686 pounds, Granular Cork	39.44 percent
413 pounds, 30 to dust	23.75 percent
TOTAL 1099 pounds, usable cork	63.19 percent
640 pounds moisture, hardback, etc.	36.80 percent

The 413 pounds of 30 to dust was clean cork suitable for use in linoleum and other products requiring fine cork.

This granulated cork was coated with binder and manufactured into composition cork rods and sheets. Exhaustive tests proved this virgin cork to be exceptionally good quality and equal in every way to imported cork of the same grade. These results gave encouragement and assurance to those who were planting cork trees. It was exciting news and brought a sharp increase in additional cork oak plantings throughout California and Arizona. More California cork trees were stripped in 1941 and each succeeding year through 1948.

In 1942 cork was removed from trees in the South and Arizona. Over

(*Courtesy, Florida Forest Service*)
Attractive young cork tree on the campus of Florida State University, Tallahassee. Age 15 years, height 22 feet, diameter, breast height, 12 inches.

three-quarters of a ton of cork was stripped from trees in Virginia, South Carolina, Georgia and Alabama, while approximately 600 pounds were taken from trees in Arizona. Like the California virgin bark this cork proved to be of very good quality when processed and manufactured into composition cork. These findings notably strengthened the Cork Project.

Removal of virgin cork from some of the domestic trees made possible the growth of reproduction cork. The formation and development of second-growth cork was closely watched. As in Europe and Africa, the growth of reproduction cork was much faster than the growth of the virgin cork. It was interesting to observe in California that in 6 years, on trees over 50 years old, more than 1 in of second-growth cork was obtained. On trees 20 years old in Georgia approximately 1 in of second-growth cork was obtained. Growth of reproduction cork in other places was entirely satisfactory. In California almost a ton of second-growth cork was harvested in 1946, 1947 and 1948. This makes possible third-growth cork which is now growing on a number of trees in California.

The quantity of cork stripped from domestic trees each year is given in the following table:

CORK STRIPPING IN THE UNITED STATES

Year	No. of Trees	Yield of Cork (lbs.)
1940	248	10,561
1941	47	2,142
1942	63	3,466
1943	46	2,735
1944	54	3,206
1945	58	3,538
1946	49	2,891
1947	38	2,318
1948	25	1,675
TOTAL	628	32,542

RESEARCH ACTIVITIES

So little was known about the culture of cork trees it was essential at the very beginning of the program to carry out all the research in this field that was possible. The study of the cork tree was divided roughly into two phases, namely, short practical tests and long range experiments. Unfortunately time did not permit these latter to be concluded, but some valuable knowledge was obtained from them.

In planting cork trees tests showed special care must be taken with bare root seedlings. The roots must be kept wet at all times while out of the ground. When planted, the earth must be packed closely about the roots and kept moist for the first two weeks. The foliage should be pruned back as the abbreviated root system is not able to supply the normal water requirements of the seedling. With the best of care and precaution, the survival of transplanted bare-root cork seedlings is low.

(*Courtesy, Division of Forestry, Dept. of Conservation, Alabama*)

This cork tree on the Capitol lawn in Montgomery, Alabama, has grown rapidly. Approximately 16 ft high and 10 in in diameter.

The recommended method for planting cork seedlings is to grow the trees 10 or 12 in high in 1-gallon cans and then place the trees with the earth intact about the roots in their permanent locations. This procedure prevents injury or exposure of the roots and the little trees receive no shock. Growth is not interrupted and the percentage of survival is very high.

A young cork tree has a long, vigorous tap root with few laterals. In lifting seedlings from a nursery bed this root is often cut and growth of the tree, if it survives transplanting, is greatly retarded. Root pruning the seedlings in the nursery when 1 year old has resulted in the development of several lateral roots. In this condition the cork seedling, when 2 years old, is better able to survive transplanting. In fact, the root pruning may be repeated the second year, causing even more lateral roots to develop. Root pruning is now recommended for all nursery grown cork seedlings when 1 year old. They may be lifted and transplanted 1 year later.

The cork oak has been grafted to native oaks.[76] The grafting experiments were carried out at the University of California. Successful grafts were made to both evergreen and deciduous native oaks. Trees from the grafts made in California are growing under observation but it will be some years yet before the trees will show whether the experiment is successful or not.

Efforts to root cork oak cuttings were successful in Georgia. The cuttings were taken in November from an old tree having excellent quality cork and producing a large annual crop of acorns. This method of propagation supplements plantings with acorns and guarantees reproduction of the tree from which the cutting is taken.

Preliminary results of plant food tests made on cork seedlings grown in sand show the cork tree responds well to calcium and nitrogen, provided all other essential elements are present. These tests show also that a good supply of plant food and water will increase the rate of growth. The soil should be slightly acid. Barnyard compost is recommended for the average tree and commercial fertilizer may be used alone or with compost.

During the 10 years that elapsed from its conception to termination, the Cork Project recorded numerous noteworthy accomplishments. The chief purpose of the endeavor was to grow cork trees in this country. In carrying out this purpose a number of related important tasks were completed. The work of the cork program made significant contributions to the knowledge and technique of planting cork trees. Much of this knowledge is applicable to other oak trees and hardwood trees in general. Some of the tangible accomplishments are given below:

1. Developed a safe method for storing and handling perishable cork oak acorns.
2. Developed a practical, efficient method for planting cork acorns.
3. Showed that root-pruning of 1-year-old cork seedlings in the nursery caused additional roots to develop.

4. Proved the cork oak could be grafted to native oaks.
5. Showed that cork oak cuttings could be made to develop roots.
6. Accurately mapped the area in the United States where the cork tree will grow well.
7. Showed cork from trees grown in the United States was comparable to that from Mediterranean cork oaks.

CHAPTER XIII

POTENTIAL CORK AREAS IN THE UNITED STATES

Then here's to the oak, the brave old oak,
Who stands in his pride alone!
And still flourish he, a hale green tree,
When a hundred years are gone!

HENRY FOTHERGILL CHORLEY

THE cork oak makes an excellent ornamental shade tree. Being an evergreen its dark green foliage during winter months is a delightful contrast to the bare limbs of deciduous trees. For this reason many home owners desire to grow cork trees. Therefore it is important to know in which states and in what parts of these states the cork oak may be expected to thrive and grow.

It is obvious that cork trees will grow where old cork oaks have grown or are growing at the present time. Accordingly, the cork tree can be grown successfully in Virginia, North Carolina, South Carolina, Georgia, Florida, Alabama, Mississippi, Louisiana, Texas, Arkansas, Arizona and California. Certainly, the warmer portions of adjoining states, with climate comparable to that of the areas which have produced mature cork trees, also may be favorable for cork plantings. For this reason Oklahoma, Tennessee, Kentucky, Maryland, Oregon and Washington along with the above-named states were asked to cooperate with the McManus Cork Project. This they did enthusiastically and helpfully and extensive plantings were made in various sections of these states annually from 1942 to 1949 inclusive.

Meanwhile, further efforts were made to determine with more certainty the complete potential cork area in the United States. A detailed study of the temperature, rainfall and soil conditions of the cork forest regions of Europe and northern Africa was made and the data obtained compared with the climate and soil throughout the United States. From this study a map was prepared showing the potential cork areas in the United States[77]. This map included all of the states referred to above and in addition parts of Delaware, New Jersey, Illinois, Indiana, Missouri and New Mexico. Limited cork plantings were made in these last-named states and, in addition, small cork planting tests were carried out in other states.

(*Courtesy, Crown Cork & Seal Co.*)

Stripping cork from a 50-year-old tree in Kearney Park, Fresno, California.

The map shows a large area in the warmer half of the United States is favorable for growing cork trees. There are three important factors that control whether the cork tree will grow in an area and, if so, how well. Temperature is a very critical growth factor. In general those sections where the mean annual temperature ranges from 50° to 80°F are favorable for the cork tree. The greater portion of the entire Mediterranean cork area lies between 50° and 60° average January temperatures. The average July temperature in the Mediterranean cork area is between 70° to 80°. This means those sections of the United States where the average January temperature is 50°F or slightly warmer and which have an average July temperature of about 80° are favorable for growing cork trees. However, cork oaks may grow well where the July temperatures average higher than 80°. In the Mediterranean area the summers are dry while in the southern portion of the United States summer rainfall compensates for temperatures above 80°. It should be kept in mind the cork oak is a temperate zone plant and will not thrive in tropical areas. Also, some cork trees can be grown under conditions colder than a January average of 50° but growth will be slower and loss of trees greater than normal. To some it is a challenge to grow plants beyond their normal temperature range. This is being done with the cork oak which becomes a deciduous tree in these sections.

Rainfall is important to the cork oak. In the Mediterranean area most of the cork forests grow where annual rainfall averages between 20 and 60 in. This, then, is the ideal quantity of water for cork trees. However, they grow in more arid regions, as well as where annual rainfall exceeds 60 in. In its native area the summers are dry and the winters constitute the rainy season. California weather closely resembles the cork Mediterranean climate, but vigorous cork trees have been growing in the southern portion of the United States for 100 years where rainfall is generous during the summer months.

Soil is the third vital factor in plant growth. The cork oak in its Mediterranean environment appears to have no specific soil requirements. The soils in the cork forests range from sandy coastal plain soils to the stony and droughty soils of the hills. In general the soils of Mediterranean cork areas are not very fertile and are incapable of supporting the growth of agricultural products without fertilization and, in many places, irrigation.

The above discussion shows the cork oak may be grown in the United States where winter temperatures are moderate. Rainfall and soil while important factors are not as critical as temperature. A short review of cork plantings in the states of the potential cork-growing area will serve to emphasize further where cork trees will grow in this country.

California has several thousand mature cork trees and it is very evident the cork oak can be grown successfully over the greater part of the state. At Chico, in Bidwell Park, stands an attractive grove of about 600 trees which were planted in 1904. Scattered throughout the states are other interesting cork oak groves. Among these are the trees at Napa State Hospital, the large trees in Kearney Park at Fresno, the many splendid specimens in the fig garden area near Fresno and the unique highway planting at Chatsworth. Supplementing these are numerous individual and small groups of trees from Humbolt County in the northern part of the state to San Diego in the southern section. With so many local examples of how well the cork tree grows in California thousands of cork trees were planted through the McManus Project and additional plantings

(Courtesy, Crown Cork & Seal Co.)
Attractive cork oak shade tree at Augusta, Georgia.

are made every year. These recent plantings, like the old cork trees, are growing well over a large section of the state.

Arizona ranks next to California in the number of mature cork trees, about 40 having been located in the state. The oldest tree which is at Superior dates back to 1879 and there are a number of attractive trees about 30 to 40 years old. More cork trees are growing in and around Phoenix than in any other section of the state. However, there are large specimens in Tucson, Tempe, Superior and Chandler. Many young cork trees are now growing in various parts of the state as a result of planting activities in the past 15 years. In areas which are irrigated the cork trees are vigorous and make normal yearly growth.

Virginia is the most northern state in the eastern part of the potential cork area in which old cork trees are growing or have grown. Richmond, Norfolk, Capeville and Onancock are places where cork trees have thrived. Limited recent plantings have added other cork oaks to these. The best examples of the young trees can be found at Gloucester Point and at the College of William and Mary in Williamsburg. Other young cork trees are growing in the potential cork area of Virginia which is in the Tidewater Section of the state.

Five mature cork trees have been located in North Carolina. These are located at Merry Hill, Raleigh, Tarboro and Manley. A very large cork tree grew at Rockingham about 30 years ago. Many cork plantings were made in North Carolina during the past 15 years. A beautiful cork tree stands on the State Capitol grounds in Raleigh and in the southern half of the eastern part of the state other examples of young cork trees can be found.

South Carolina is rich in cork oak history. The earliest record of a cork tree in this country reported one in South Carolina and Thomas Jefferson made repeated efforts to establish cork trees at Charleston (see Chapter X). Today South Carolina possesses a number of mature cork trees and shows evidence of others that thrived some years ago. The distribution of these trees indicates practically the entire state is well suited for growing cork trees. Many plantings have been made in recent years and today vigorous young cork trees can be found throughout the state.

One young cork tree is growing on the State House Grounds and South Carolina was the first state to have a cork tree planted at its capitol by the governor of the state. Governor Olin D. Johnston, now United States Senator, was the first governor to plant a cork tree in a state-wide observance of arbor day. Other young cork trees are at Bishopville, Clemson, Columbia, Aiken and Barnwell.

Georgia has more mature cork trees than any other southern state. They are growing at Augusta, Columbus, Atlanta, Ocilla and other parts of the state. Augusta has more cork trees than any other place in Georgia, there being more than a dozen in this city. One of the oldest is on the National Golf Course and was planted about 1859. Some of the other cork trees in this area apparently resulted from acorns from this very old

H

tree. The largest cork tree in Georgia is at Georgetown and measures 45 inches in diameter. Two very old cork trees are growing at Sparta and one at Atlanta has been severely injured several times but continues to be a vigorous tree. A magnificent cork tree recently grew at McDonough where it had provided shade for four generations of the family by which the tree was planted. Two grand old cork oaks in Columbus are still

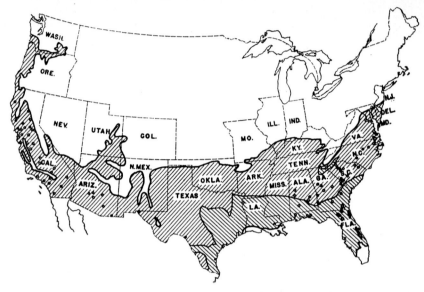

(*Courtesy, Smithsonian Institution*)

Potential cork areas in the United States.

vigorous. There are records of a number of cork trees that formerly grew in the state.

A cork tree is growing at Georgia's State Capitol which was planted by Governor Ellis G. Arnall in 1944. Many cork plantings were made in Georgia by Future Farmers of America from 1944 to 1949. These plantings have produced young cork trees in all parts of the state. Some of these trees may be seen at Alto, Plains, Jakin, Colquitt, Statesboro and Macon.

Florida, also, is a potential cork-growing area. A special planting was made near Pensacola in 1914 by the U.S. Forest Service. Practically all of these trees were destroyed by a severe storm 3 years later, but several have survived. Large cork trees have grown in Tallahassee and Lake City. The long growing season and mild winters in northern Florida made this area favorable for cork oak plantings. Florida has young cork trees from recent plantings which have grown well in Jacksonville, Graceville, Tampa and Tallahassee. On the Capitol grounds in Tallahassee a cork tree planted by former Governor Holland, now United States Senator, has grown to attractive size.

Alabama has interesting examples of large cork trees as well as records of others that lived to old age and died. In 1942 a large cork tree grew at Greensboro that had been planted in 1858. At Autaugaville stands an enormous cork tree—44 in in diameter. Another large cork tree grew at Hybart and records show large cork oaks have grown at Greenville and Benton. A tree at Tuscaloosa is vigorous and thriving. From plantings of the McManus Project there are numerous young cork trees in many parts of the state. Some of these may be seen at Mobile, Frisco City, Ozark, Gadsden and on the State House grounds in Montgomery.

At Shreveport, Louisiana, a group of vigorous 35-year-old cork trees indicates parts of this state are well suited to the cork oak. But equally convincing are the literature references to cork trees in the state. An item written in 1912 was illustrated with a picture of corkbark from a Louisiana cork tree. The cork was about $1\frac{1}{2}$ in thick which showed the tree was at least 40 years old at that time. Thus, it has been evident for some time the climate and soil of sections of Louisiana are favorable for growing cork trees. Shreveport also has attractive young cork trees and in Baton Rouge a cork tree planted by Governor Davis can be seen on the State Capitol grounds.

In Texas old cork trees are growing at El Paso and Del Rio. The specimens are vigorous and healthy showing the suitability of the drier sections for the cork tree. Results of plantings made by the McManus Project have been excellent, especially in the Houston area. Here many ornamental cork oak shade trees are growing. Other locations of cork trees 15 ft to 25 ft high are Mission, Alvin, Palestine, Port Author and College Station. A young cork tree at Houston about 15 years old is now bearing acorns. This tree had a good acorn yield in the fall of 1957.

Mississippi has attractive cork trees at Wiggins, Moss Point and Tupelo. One planted at Jackson on the Capitol grounds by former Governor Bailey has grown slowly.

Other states have numerous young cork trees. One in Nashville, Tennessee, which was planted by former Governor McCord has grown slowly. A cork tree on the Capitol grounds at Little Rock, Arkansas, planted by former Governor Laney, also has made little progress. Cork trees are growing at Enid, Oklahoma, and elsewhere in the state. A number of cork trees are growing slowly in the Baltimore, Maryland area, and they are growing in sections of Oregon.

Records show the cork oak grows well in the areas discussed above. The tree is excellent for ornamental shade purposes and offers a variation from the usual shade trees. The young cork trees now growing in the warmer parts of the country are beginning to yield acorns. This seed is acclimated to the sections where it is produced and should be planted in that area. In a few more years thousands of homes in each of the states of the potential cork area can have evergreen cork oak shade trees.

In 1948 V. A. Ryan completed his study of potential cork areas in the United States.[78] Individual maps showing soil, rainfall and temperature conditions favorable to the cork tree were prepared. In addition, a composite map covering these three important growth factors was prepared. The new composite map indicates the cork oak will grow in all, or parts, of twenty-seven states.

CHAPTER XIV

PROPAGATION OF CORK TREES

How many an acorn falls to die for one that makes
a tree.

JOHN BANISTER TABB

FOR many years the propagation of cork trees was the result of natural seeding. With the increased demands for cork in the past 100 years the governments of the cork-growing countries, as well as some private owners of cork forests, have aided in the maintenance and extension of cork-growing areas. This interest in reforestation and planting additional land in cork oaks has focused attention on the most practical methods of growing the trees. The best procedure may depend upon several factors.

Experienced cork foresters recommend direct seeding as both the most efficient and most economical method for planting cork trees. Growing seedlings in a nursery and transplanting to the selected area is practiced to some extent. No particular effort appears to have been made toward rooting cuttings from trees producing superior cork or in grafting scions from selected trees to small cork oak seedlings or to seedlings of other oak trees.

In the warmer parts of the United States the cork oak grows well and is becoming popular as a shade tree. Its thick green foliage during the winter season is a delightful contrast to the bare limbs of deciduous trees. As the name implies a shade tree must be of such character that it provides shade. In addition it is highly desirable that a shade tree be ornamental. A tree that has some economic value besides giving shade and possessing beauty approaches the ideal. The cork oak is such a tree. With its long spreading branches and heavy evergreen foliage the cork oak is an excellent shade tree. Its bark is the valuable cork of commerce and its large acorns which are produced in generous quantities serve well as a supplemental stock food. In the cork oak nature generously has combined usefulness with beauty.

Cork oaks for ornamental purposes are planted in small numbers. Home owners are interested in fast growth in order that the tree will become attractive at an early age. Planting and growing small numbers of cork trees requires special techniques. However, the general characteristics of the tree are the same whether planted for shade or in cork forests. The same special care must be given to the acorns and seedlings.

(*Courtesy, Crown Cork & Seal Co.*)

Sacks of mature acorns ready for planting.

There are several methods of planting cork oaks as ornamental shade trees, the simplest of which is planting acorns. This is nature's method of propagation and given a fair chance is highly successful. A mature cork oak produces generous quantities of acorns which ripen and fall from the tree in November and December. Cork acorns will sprout in a short time if left under the tree. They are very perishable and special care must be taken to prevent drying after the acorns are collected. In order to save the cork acorns they should be gathered as soon as possible after ripening. In areas where the winters are mild the acorns may be planted as soon as possible after they are gathered. Where winter weather drops to freezing and below the planting may be deferred until spring. Cork acorns for spring planting should be kept in wet cold storage. The low temperature range (34° to 38°F.) holds the acorns dormant and viable for several months. When removed from wet cold storage the acorns should be planted promptly for they begin to sprout quickly after returning to normal temperature.

The ideal way to grow cork trees is to plant an acorn where the tree is to grow. This can easily be done and it eliminates future transplanting with the usual root damage and shock to the seedling. The ground should be well prepared—an area about 3 feet in diameter. Of course, rich soil speeds the growth of a tree and in preparing the ground some compost and fertilizer may be worked into the soil. This additional plant food is

(*Courtesy, Crown Cork & Seal Co.*)

Cork acorns should be planted in well-prepared permanent locations. Three acorns should be planted but after sprouting, the smaller two should be removed and transplanted.

exhausted while the tree is still young and does not interfere with the formation of good cork. In order to make certain a good tree will be obtained in every location, three acorns should be planted at each spot. When the seedlings are about 6 or 8 inches high, the small, weaker ones are removed and transplanted, the most vigorous seedling remaining in each site.

Squirrels, gophers and rodents eat cork acorns and care must be taken to protect each planting from such destruction. The simplest and safest procedure is to place a small wire cage over each acorn or each planting. Sometimes covering the ground with suitable screen wire will suffice. Discarded 5-quart cans are also effective. The bottom should be cut away and the cylinder placed over the planting and pressed into the ground about 3 inches. Attempts have been made to treat the acorn with suitable chemicals to prevent destruction by small animals. At the present time only partial success has been achieved by these efforts and the only sure safeguard is mechanical protection.

Directions for Planting Cork Oak Acorns

Before cork acorns are received:

1. Select planting locations about 30 feet apart.
2. Clean spots, 3 feet in diameter, of weeds and grass.
3. Prepare the soil well in each spot.

When cork acorns have been received:

1. Place cork acorns in well-prepared moist earth of permanent locations, 3 feet in diameter, and cover with an inch of soil. Plant three cork acorns to the spot, spaced about 6 inches apart. Place a marker, a 2- to 3-foot stick, in center of each spot.

2. Squirrels and rodents are fond of cork acorns. Do everything possible to protect the plantings from them. Old wire window screens, rainspout screens or 5-quart cans with ends removed may be used.

3. When seedlings are 6 inches high, thin each spot to one, using extra seedlings for replanting blank spots or for planting in new locations. In removing extra cork seedlings for transplanting *leave a large ball of earth* about the roots, and place seedlings in well-prepared ground.

4. Keep grass and weeds out of each 3-foot area. Mulch the young seedlings with leaves or similar material. This conserves moisture in dry weather and retards the growth of grass and weeds.

5. During prolonged dry weather cork seedlings should be watered.

6. Should top of plant die do not disturb the area. Often these plants will put forth from beneath the surface of the ground and finally make good trees. Sometimes trees will die back once or twice and then come back in the spring in this manner.

Planting Cork Seedlings

Cork trees for ornamental purposes may be propagated by planting seedlings grown in a nursery. A high percentage of survival is attained when the seedlings are produced in individual containers. This may be carried out in greenhouses in sections where winter temperatures are frequently below freezing. However, caution should be exercised in watering the seedlings in the greenhouse. Too frequent applications of water accelerates the growth and a tender plant with a profusion of foliage results. Such seedlings after being planted outside in permanent locations may have difficulty surviving a hot, dry period in the summer or a cold wave during winter.

Where the winters are mild cork seedlings may be grown in the open in individual containers. During cool weather growth will be slow but the plants will be healthy and hardy. Seedlings grown in this manner show good resistance against hot, dry summer weather and cold temperatures in winter. During the growing season the seedlings make good growth.

Various kinds of containers may be used for growing cork seedlings. The cork oak has a long tap root and shallow vessels should be avoided unless the seedlings are transplanted to permanent sites while very small. Discarded 1-gallon cans are suitable but shorter cans restrict normal root

(*Courtesy, Crown Cork & Seal Co.*)

Cork seedlings should be staked for protection and mulched.

development. The bottoms should have holes about 2 inches in diameter cut in the center or they may be removed entirely. The cans may be placed on any convenient flat place where drainage is good or on a board. The soil will form a compact mass about the roots as the seedling develops, permitting necessary moving of the container. If the seedling is shipped, some support must be provided at the bottom to hold the soil in place.

Waterproofed paper pots, tubes and cylinders have been used successfully for growing cork seedlings. Tubes 12 in long and 3 in in diameter may be prepared from waterproofed roofing paper. Sheets 12 in by 10 in are rolled into a cylinder and the overlapping edges stapled. Ordinary paper tubes of suitable dimensions may be employed by waterproofing them with paraffin or other low cost materials that are not injurious to plants.

When the seedlings are transplanted to permanent locations it is not necessary to remove the container. A hole large enough to receive the metal can or paper tube should be prepared and the seedling in the container placed in the ground. The paper or metal will disintegrate in a reasonable time and will not appreciably retard the growth of the plant.

I

In cases where the earth in the container is firm and compact and can be handled without crumbling, the paper or metal may be cut away from the ball of earth. By transplanting cork seedlings in this way, possible injury to the roots is avoided and growth is not delayed by plant shock.

Cork seedlings which have been grown in a nursery may be root pruned when 1 year old. The main or tap roots are cut about 8 in

(Courtesy, Texas Forest Service)
A vigorous young cork tree at College Station, Texas.

below the level of the ground and the seedlings left in the nursery for another year. This stimulates root growth and results in more lateral roots for the seedlings. The same seedlings may be root pruned a second time the following year and kept in the nursery for 3 years. When transplanted, root-pruned seedlings should have the foliage cut back to reduce plant respiration. The roots should be kept wet until the seedlings are replanted.

PLANTING INSTRUCTIONS

Before cork seedlings are received:

1. Select the planting locations 30 feet apart.
2. Clean areas 3 feet in diameter of weeds, grass and other vegetation.
3. Prepare the soil well in each area.

After cork seedlings are received:

A. Seedlings in Paper Pots.

1. Make holes in the soft, well-prepared ground with a garden trowel as deep as the containers are high.
2. Open the paper folds and remove seedling with ball of earth about the roots.
3. Place seedling in the ground and press earth firmly about the roots. Water moderately.
4. Place stake near tree and tie tree loosely with twine or rag to stake.
5. Keep grass and weeds out of each 3-foot area.
6. Mulch the young seedlings with leaves or similar material. This conserves moisture in dry weather and retards the growth of grass and weeds.
7. Water the seedlings the first summer about once a week, during prolonged hot, dry periods.

B. Seedlings in Cans.

1. Make holes in the soft, well-prepared ground with a garden trowel as deep as the containers are high.
2. Make certain bottom of can has been cut away.
3. Place seedling in container in the ground, pack earth firmly about can and water moderately.
4. Follow directions 4 to 7 inclusive as given under A above.

C. Bare-root Seedlings.

1. Plant the cork seedlings the same day they are received.
2. Make holes in the soft, well-prepared ground with a garden trowel as deep as the seedling roots are long. Place seedling in hole at same depth as it was before.
3. Half-fill hole with dirt. Then pour water with full force into hole.
4. Finish filling hole with dry dirt and pack soil lightly.

5. Place stake near tree and tie tree loosely with twine or rag to stake.
6. Keep grass and weeds out of each 3-foot area.
7. Mulch the young seedlings with leaves or similar material. This conserves moisture in dry weather and also retards the growth of grass and weeds.
8. Water the seedlings the first summer about once a week, during prolonged hot, dry periods.

Note: When planting the seedlings, keep the roots in a bucket of water or wrapped in wet burlap, removing only one tree at a time.

Spacing the seedlings, or acorns, 30 feet apart will give approximately fifty plantings to the acre. The success of any planting depends largely on the care and attention given the little trees the first several years. While they are small the cork trees should be pruned and trained so they will grow and develop into attractive, beautiful trees.

CHAPTER XV

FUTURE TRENDS

I know of no way of judging the future but
by the past.

PATRICK HENRY

HAVING attained its primary purpose of establishing a number of cork trees in the potential cork oak area of the United States the Cork Project was terminated early in 1949. While the number of cork trees growing at that time was not large reports showed the number to be sufficiently high to yield a limited quantity of mature trees. Today, after a 10-year period during which these cork trees have grown well and are of medium size, the status of the cork oak in this country can be evaluated with reasonable accuracy.

The place of the cork oak here will be that of an ornamental shade tree. It has served such a purpose for 100 years on a very small scale. In the past 15 years this exotic oak tree has become much better known. Many people have become acquainted with this attractive tree and more are learning about it every year. The cork oak will become more and more popular as a shade tree in the warmer half of the United States. Those who now have young cork trees have found they blend well with other trees and shrubs to provide a new and delightful appearance to homes, both suburban and rural. The cork oak has proven to be a distinctly pleasing addition to the usual, familiar evergreen trees and provides a new range and variety in landscape gardening.

As the young cork trees now flourishing continue their growth and begin bearing acorns cork plantings will become more numerous. Acorns produced from these trees will be planted near their place of origin. Trees from these acorns will be acclimated to their particular location. They will make vigorous growth and will be hardy. With the yearly quantity of cork acorns becoming larger as the trees increase in size more and more trees will be planted. The next decade will witness an upsurge of attention to the cork oak as a shade tree.

The future of cork in the United States will follow the trends established in recent years. Cork products will continue to be in demand in about the same quantity with some possible expansion. New substitutes will appear from time to time for special applications while in other fields the use of cork may expand. New applications of cork will be found and new products containing cork will be developed. Cork imports have shown some increase during the past 10 years and in the immediate future will enjoy the same demands. The nation's cork requirements will continue to come from the Mediterranean area as in the past. The world's cork of commerce will be produced by the cork forests of Europe and Africa.

Thus cork, which has been an important material to man for thousands of years and a valuable commercial commodity for centuries, will continue to be needed. The tree from which it comes will in this country, and perhaps elsewhere, be grown for ornamental shade purposes.

LITERATURE CITED

1. *Plutarch's Lives*, II, Chap. XXV, 155. Eng. Trans. by Bernadotte Perin. New York, Macmillan (1914).
2. PLINY, *Natural History*, XVI, Chap. 13. Eng. Trans. Cambridge, Mass., Harvard Univ. Press, IV, 410–11 (1938).
3. HORACE, *Odes*, III, Ode 8, 79, Oxford, E. C. Wickham. Trans. by C. Smart. New York, Harper (1871).
4. COLUMELLA, *De Re Rustica*, IX, Chap. VI. Trans. Columella of Husbandry by A. Miller. London (1745).
5. VIRGIL'S Works. *The Aeneid, Eclogues, Georgics*. Eng. Trans. by J. W. Mackail. New York, Random House (1950).
6. THEOPHRASTUS, *Enquiry into Plants*, III, Chap. XVII. Eng. Trans. by Sir Arthur Hort, I, 265. New York, Putnam (1916).
7. PAUSANIAS, *Description of Greece*, VIII, Chap. XII, 1. Eng. Trans. by W. H. S. Jones, III, 405. New York, Putnam (1918).
8. CERVANTES, *Don Quixote*. Eng. Trans. by Samuel Putnam. New York, The Viking Press (1958).
9. SHAKESPEARE, WILLIAM, *The Winter's Tale*, Act. III, Scene III. New York, Walter J. Black.
10. PEPYS, SAMUEL, *Diary*, Mynors Bright. New York, Random House (1946).
11. *Cork In Spain*, The Ministry of Commerce, Economic Studies Section. Madrid (1954).
12. CAMUS, A., *Les Chenes, Q. Suber*. Paris, Paul Lechevalier (1936–38).
13. WILLIAMS, SIMON, *Bull. Torrey Bot. C.*, **66**, 353 (1939), **69**, 1 and 115 (1942).
14. LAMEY, A., *Le Chene Liege, Sa Culture et son Exploitation*. Paris, Berger-Levrault et cie (1893).
15. MULLER, E. A., *Uber Die Korkeiche*, Wein (1900).
16. GOIS, ER. DA S. R., Arborization of Land South of the River Tagus with Cork Oak Trees. *Junta Nacional da Cortica*, No. 205 (Nov. 1955).
17. NATIVIDADE, J. V., Selection and Genetic Improvement of the Cork Oak in Portugal, *Rev. for Fr.* **6**, 346–354 (1954); per *Plant Breed. Abstr.*, **25**, 2410 (1955).
18. *Quart. J. For.*, VII, 37, U.S. Dept. Agri.
19. SMITH, J. RUSSELL, *Tree Crops*, 135–137. New York, Harcourt, Brace & Co. (1929).
20. NATIVIDADE, J. V., *Suberculture*. Lisbon (1950).
21. HOOKE, ROBERT, *Micrographia*. London, J. Martyn and J. Allestry (1665).
22. LEWIS, FRED. T., The Shape of Cork Cells, *Science* 68 (Dec. 21, 1928).
23. DART, S. L. and GUTH, E., The Elastic Properties of Cork. Pub. in *High Polymer Physics*, Robinson, H. A. Brooklyn, Chem. Pub. Co. (1948).
24. BRUGNATELLI, D. L., *Ann. Chim.*, Bd. I, St. 2, 145–148 (1787).
25. LA GRANGE, B., *Ann. Chim.*, **23**, 48–56 (1797).

26. CHEVREUL, M., *Ann. Chim.*, **62,** 323 (1807); **96,** 141 (1815).
27. BOUSSINGAULT, J., *C.R. Acad., Sci. Paris*, **2,** 77 (1836).
28. DOPPING, O., *Liebigs Ann.* **45,** 286 (1843).
29. SIEWART, M., *J. Pr. Chem.*, **104,** 118 (1863).
30. KÜGHER, K., *Arch. Pharm.*, **22,** 217 (1884).
31. FRIEDEL, C., *Bull. Soc. Chim.* (3) **7,** 164 (1892).
32. THOMS, H., *Pharm. Zentralh.*, **39,** 699 (1898).
33. ISTRATI, C. and OSTROGORICH, A., *C.R. Acad. Sci. Paris*, **128,** 1581 (1899).
34. DRAKE, N. L. and JACOBSEN, R. P., *J. Amer. Chem. Soc.*, **57,** 1570 (1935).
35. DRAKE, N. L. and SHRADER, S. A., *J. Amer. Chem. Soc.*, **57,** 1854 (1935).
36. DRAKE, N. L. and CAMPBELL, W. P., *J. Amer. Chem. Soc.*, **58,** 1681 (1936).
37. DRAKE, N. L. and HASKINS, W. T., *J. Amer. Chem. Soc.*, **58,** 1684 (1936).
38. DRAKE, N. L. and WOLFE, J. K., *J. Amer. Chem. Soc.*, **61,** 3074 (1939).
39. COREY, E. J. and URSPRUNG, J. J., *J. Amer. Chem. Soc.*, **78,** 5041 (1956).
40. ZEMPLEN, G., *Z. Physiol. Chem.*, **85,** 173 (1913).
41. VON HOHNEL, F., *S.B. Wiener Akad.*, **76,** I, 527 (1877).
42. GILSON, E., *La Cellule*, **6,** 63 (1890).
43. VON SCHMIDT, M., *Monatsh.*, **25,** 277, 302 (1904); **31,** 347 (1910).
44. SCURTI, F. and TOMMASI, G., *Gazz. chim. ital.*, **46,** pt. 2, 159 (1916). *Ann. Staz. Chimagr. Roma*, II, **6,** 40, 53, 67 (1917). *ibid.*, II, **9,** 145 (1920).
45. ZETSCHE, F. and ROSENTHAL, G., *Helv. Chim. Acta*, **10,** 346 (1927).
46. ZETSCHE, F., CHOLATNIKOV, C., and SCHERZ, K., *Helv. Chim. Acta*, **11,** 272 (1928).
47. ZETSCHE, F. and SONDEREGGER, G., *Helv. Chim. Acta.* **14,** 632 (1931).
48. ZETSCHE, F. and BÄHLER, M., *Helv. Chim. Acta*, **14,** 852 (1931).
49. ZETSCHE, F. and WEBER, KURT, *J. Prakt. Chem.*, **150,** 140 (1938).
50. DRAKE, N. L., CARHART, H. W., and MOZINGO, R. J., *J. Amer. Chem. Soc.*, **63,** 617 (1941).
51. ERLENMEYER, H., and MÜLLER, M., *Verh. Naturforsch Ges.*, **56,** 11 and 366 (1945).
52. GUILLEMONAT, A. and STRICH, A., *Bull, Soc. Chim.*, 360 (1950).
53. RIBAS, I. and CURBERA, G., *Ann. Soc. Esp. Fis. y Quim.*, 47B, 639 and 713 (1951).
54. JENSEN, W., *Paper and Timber (Finland)*, **32,** 261–6 (1950).
55. MULDER, *Physiol. Chem.*, 507 (1844).
56. PAYEN, M., *C.R. Acad. Sci. Paris*, 509 (1868).
57. WIESNER, J., *Zitiert nach Czopek*, I.C.S. 696.
58. HABERLAND, O., *Ostera. Bot Z.*, No. 8 (1874).
59. FREMY, E., and URBAIN, *J. Pharm. Chim. Paris*, **5,** 113 (1883).
60. VAN WISSELING, H., *Arch. Neerland, Sci. exact. et nat.*, **12** (1888).
61. KARRER, P., PEYER, J. and ZEGA, Z., *Helv. Chim. Acta*, **5,** 583 (1923), 853 (1922).
62. MADINAVEITIZ, A., OLAY, E., and CATALAN, T., *La Farmica Moderna, Madried*, **46,** 827 (1935).
63. STOCKAR, G. K., *Promotionsarbeit*, Zurich (1948).
64. HAAS, P., and HILL, T., *The Chemistry of Plant Products*, Vol. I, New York, Longmans, Green and Co., 1928.
65. RIBAS, I. and BLASCO, E., *Ann. Soc. Esp. Fis. y Quim.*, **36,** 141 (1940).
66. ZETSCHE, F. and LÜSHER, E., *J. Prakt. Chem.*, 150, 68–80 (1927).
67. WARTH, A. H., *The Chemistry and Technology of Waxes*, Reinhold, New York, 1956.

68. GUILLEMONAT, A., *Bull. Soc. Chim. Fr.*, **9**, 195 and 589 (1942).

69. BARCELO, J., *Ann. Soc. Esp. Fis. y Quim.*, **35**, 107 (1939).

70. FAUBEL, A. L., *Cork and the American Cork Industry*. New York, Cork Institute of America (1941).

71. THOMAS, P. E., *Cork Insulation*. Chicago, Nickerson and Collins (1928).

72. BARTRAM, JOHN, *Diary of a Journey through the Carolinas, Georgia and Florida*, Philadelphia. Trans. Amer. Phil. Soc., Vol. 33, Pt. 1 (1942).

73. JEFFERSON, THOMAS, *Letters*. Washington, D.C., The Library of Congress.

74. HOUGH, F. B., *Reports of Forestry*. Washington, D.C., U.S. Dept. Agri.

75. METCALF, WOODBRIDGE, Cork Oak, A Forest Tree with Possibilities for California. *Monthly Bull.* 18, No. 10, Sacramento, Cal., State Dept. of Agric. (1929).

76. MIROV, N. T. and CUMMING, W. C., Propagation of Cork Oak by Grafting. *J. For.*, **43**, 589–591 (1945).

77. RYAN, VICTOR A., *Potential Cork Areas in the United States*. Baltimore, Crown Cork & Seal Co. (1942).

78. RYAN, VICTOR A. and COOKE, GILES, B., *The Cork Oak in the United States*. The Smithsonian Report for 1948.

SUBJECT INDEX

INDEX OF PLACES AND PERSONS
NOT IN LITERATURE REFERENCES

Date Due